# WALLER'S DESCRIPTION of the
# MINES in CARDIGANSHIRE

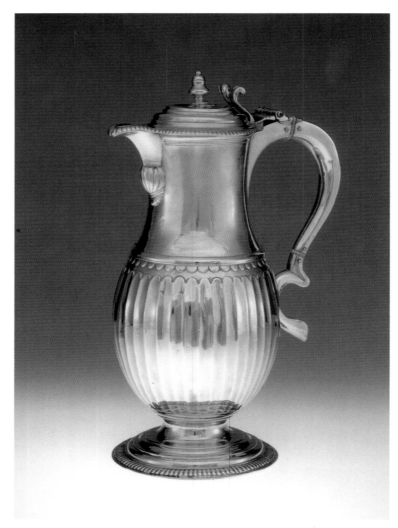

A silver ewer inscribed *The Mines of Bwlch-yr-Eskir-hir*, c.1692 (*NMW* )

# WALLER'S DESCRIPTION of the MINES in CARDIGANSHIRE

David Bick

Black Dwarf Publications

*To William Waller and all his Works*

**Note:** Permission should be obtained before entering private land but most or all of the mines described here can be viewed from public rights of way. They are not without hazard, so please be careful.

© **Black Dwarf Publications and David Bick 2004**
Designed by Neil Parkhouse, and David and William Bick

British Library Cataloguing-in-Publication Data. A catalogue
record for this book is available from the British Library
**ISBN 1 903599 11 3**

**Black Dwarf Publications**
**120 Farmer's Close, Witney, Oxfordshire OX28 1NR**
**Unit 144B, Lydney Trading Estate, Harbour Road, Lydney, Gloucestershire GL15 4EJ**

Black Dwarf Publications is an imprint of Black Dwarf Lightmoor
**website: www.lightmoor.co.uk**

Printed by The Alden Group, Oxford

# CONTENTS

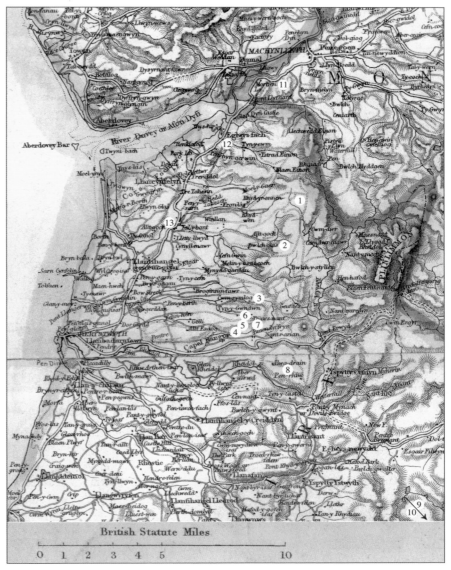

North Cardiganshire, from a map of Wales by Edward Weller, c.1830s. The numbers have been added to correspond with Waller's key map.

# PART 1

## INTRODUCTION

'Of ancient writ unlock the learned store,
Consult the dead and live past ages o'er.'
*Alexander Pope*

William Waller's *A Description of the Mines in Cardiganshire* is one of the most valuable printed sources in the history of British metal mining. Best known for its key map of the silver-lead mines worked by the Company of Mine Adventurers, the book also contains intriguing descriptions of individual sites, illustrated by the earliest known plans of mine workings. By a happy coincidence, 2004 marks its tercentenary and a fitting occasion for the present publication, so that a wider audience might appreciate the value of Waller's legacy.

The first part of this volume is devoted to the troubled world of the Mine Adventure – a remarkable and even notorious episode which has passed into the folklore of Wales. It was largely inspired by Waller with his visions of untold wealth but the reality descended into corruption, intrigue and more or less total disaster. Sir Humphrey Mackworth of Neath was also deeply involved and the story has been outlined many times[1] but there is a crying need for an in-depth account, based on extensive archives which have never received the attention they deserve. The following pages in answering certain questions raise many more but will, I hope, encourage such a project. A more fascinating and deserving study could scarcely be conceived on the subject of mining in the Principality.

The second part is a facsimile reprint of Waller's *Description*, with some added material and somewhat reset to suit the larger format. Drawing attention to these forgotten records calls to mind *Lewis Morris and the Cardiganshire Mines,* published by the National Library of Wales in 1994. Along with my series *The Old Metal Mines of Mid-Wales*, I hope it will be a useful companion, both in the study and in the field. As for the spelling of names, in those days it was pretty casual (Ystumtuen, for instance, had over a dozen variations) and, accepting defeat, my approach has been much the same. (It should also be mentioned that the letter 's' was often written as 'f'.)

Regarding the physical testimony, it is due to the unchanging nature of mid-Wales that three centuries later, at least something of every mine remains to attract our attention. However, apart from the lead mill site at Talybont, only traces at the Silver Mills and Garreg may yet survive, whilst at Neath, all lies forgotten below the sprawl of modern development.

## THE EARLY SILVER MINES

Between Plynlimon and the sea, the Silurian and Ordovician strata is riddled with mineral veins, often extending for miles. In places they have been worked for their silver-lead and copper ores, at some sites as long ago as the Bronze Age. Even at so remote a period, the orthodox view is that metallic copper was the real objective but proof beyond all doubt still remains elusive.[2] Perhaps ore for cosmetic or other purposes, or the silver content of the lead was the prize, for the best of the mines ran up to 70 oz of the precious metal to the ton of lead. Cwmsymlog was already renowned when re-opened in the 1580s, the silver going to London for minting into coinage.[3]

We know more of developments under Sir Hugh Myddelton, a London goldsmith already established in public works.[4] In 1617, he leased the mine from the Crown along with others in the region and, aided by pumping machinery, it responded well. Myddelton was soon returning large profits and, according to the records, nearly half a ton of silver went to the Tower in 1625-6. To this could be added the value of the lead reclaimed from the litharge (lead oxide) after extracting the silver by cupellation.

Thus Cwmsymlog achieved a lasting fame and, after Sir Hugh's death, the lessee was Thomas Bushell. He was a charmer but also a rogue and a favourite of the Lord Chancellor, Sir Francis Bacon. John Aubrey, a contemporary, recorded how '*he had so delicate a way of making his projects alluring and feasible, profitable, that he drewe to his baites not only rich men of no designe, but also the craftiest knaves in the country …*'.[5] Bushell lived by his wits to a ripe old age and left behind enormous debts which were never repaid. But he brought work to Wales and long afterwards local people esteemed his memory. Mining has ever attracted such characters. And in so hazardous an industry, without some vision of wealth to raise the necessary capital, few promotions would have ever left – or rather penetrated, the ground.

Bushell also leased more mines – Talybont, Goginan, Cwmerfin, Bronfloyd and later Cwmystwyth. His method was to drive deep adits to unwater the drowned workings, though it is doubtful if the method was as novel as he claimed. Before the introduction of gunpowder this was a painfully slow business but even so, Cwmsymlog and Goginan both responded. Smelting and refining was carried out at Talybont, Garreg and in the Silver Mills at Ynys-hir. The venture went well enough to justify a mint at Aberystwyth to coin the silver and some of the profits paid for clothing the army of King Charles I.[4]

## ESGAIRHIR AND ITS SILVER

After Bushell's departure about 1647, the industry did not revive to any extent until the discovery in 1689 of silver-lead ore at Esgairhir, in the hills east of Talybont, on the estate of the Pryse family. The find was so promising that, in 1691, Sir Carbery Pryse formed a company which led to the law releasing mineral owners from the incubus of the Crown's claims on precious metals. Whether or not Esgairhir was worth much in silver may be doubted but in any event an age-old brake on mining was at last removed.

Perhaps to celebrate the victory, a ewer in solid silver nearly 12 inches high was commissioned. It re-appeared 'out of the blue' at Sotheby's in 1958 and is illustrated in the frontispiece. The underneath is engraved '*The Mines of Bwlch-yr-Eskir-hir*' and the neck carries the arms of Powell of Nanteos and Pryse of Gogerddan. The late George Boon ascribed a probable date of 1692-3.[3]

Relics closely linked with mining of such antiquity are rare, and somehow seem to possess the power to annihilate all the years between.

## WALLER AND THE COMPANY OF MINE ADVENTURERS

In 1691, an energetic and colourful mining engineer from the North of England, named William Waller, was sent to inspect Esgairhir by Philip Bickerstaffe, one of Sir Carbery's partners. The visit astonished him – there was '*the largest Vein of Ore that i had ever seen, being 7 Foot 6 Inches wide in solid Ore, and was then about 13 Yards deep in Ore from the Surface.*'[6]

Waller was appointed manager a year later and the new life in virtually a foreign country cannot have been easy for him. Nonetheless, highly optimistic forecasts followed, together with a plan of the mine, reproduced on pages 14-15. In estimating the profits, he should have known that mineral lodes of this kind are uncertain things but caution was thrown aside. The expenses of mining, dressing, carriage and smelting were equally unrealistic but the presentation made it all sound plausible enough. However, his belief must have been genuine, for he offered to be paid solely out of the profits. Waller prudently made no mention of silver, since he must have known that the values were no more than average at best. However, its potential would not lie dormant for long.

Operations did not commence until 1693 but progress lagged far behind the publicity, and after a few years all work had ceased. Then, when bankruptcy seemed certain, in the words of W.R. Scott '*there appeared upon the scene Sir Humphrey Mackworth, to whom the notoriety, which marked the subsequent history of the venture, is due*'. The story of how Waller met him by chance in a public house at Llanbadarn Fawr has been told many times.[6] Mackworth was a wealthy Christian, a barrister, coal-owner, smelter and entrepreneur in want of

St HUGH MYDDELTON Knight & Baronet.

Found in a junk shop, this rare engraving by George Vertue in 1722 depicts Sir Hugh Myddelton in full regalia shortly before his death in December 1631. From a painting by Cornelius Jannson.

copper ores to feed his works in Neath, and it was from this epoch-making encounter that, to paraphrase Waller, the wheels really began to turn.

By combining forces each could envisage salvation in the other and the noble lord's social connections combined with his high Christian principles were worth more than mineral riches to aid investment. Furthermore, the reputation of the district which had been such a source of treasure in the days of Myddelton and Bushell proved a priceless asset to the promoters.

Adjoining Esgairhir to the east and on the same run of lodes was Esgairfraith, another bare and windswept mountain but, according to Waller, equally rich in mineral opportunities. Mackworth moved fast and, in December 1697, bought a lease on Esgairfraith and a little later on ground containing the adit (West Level). The transactions were hardly settled when the formation of the Governor and Company of the Mine Adventurers of England was announced. It was to be financed by a lottery, which Waller claimed was his idea.

The Duke of Leeds was made Governor with Mackworth in effect the managing director. In respect of raising capital, the results were astonishing, with £26,000 subscribed overnight (£10 million or more in today's money). To further the promotion, in the same year, 1698, Waller's well-known *Essay on the Value of the Mines late of Sir Carbery Price* was published. The book of some 75 pages, with a long preamble, repeated the original forecasts of 1693 but now with much emphasis devoted to copper and especially silver, which had scarcely been mentioned before. If not an outright swindle, it was at best a very chancy speculation and we cannot help wondering why Waller was wildly risking his name once more. Or was he simply the puppet, dancing to the strings of the master? For it now appears that Sir Humphrey Mackworth was behind the hyperbole, with the ostensible author there to carry the can.[7]

But as regards the hapless investor, it is human nature readily to believe what you very much wish to be true and the publication doubtless had the desired effect.

The venture began with gusto and a new community for a hundred miners sprang up, using prefabricated frames shipped from London. It was dubbed 'The Welsh Potosi' after the famous silver mines in South America and welfare was not ignored: *'The Houses be with all imaginable Speed erected on the Mountaine … and Covered with the best Tile.'* Better *'Hutts'* were to be installed over the shafts *'to keep the Workmen dry and Warme'*, and local people were encouraged *'to Settle on the Mountaine who may Bake Bread you to be Judge that the Workmen be not Cheated by them.'*[8]

However, it was always jam tomorrow but never jam today. The workings were frequently drowned, with the ore uncertain in quality and failing in depth. By the winter of 1699-1700, Mackworth was becoming frantic, ever pressing for glowing reports, the prototypes of those sent in by their thousand to the *Mining Journal* over a century later: *'I must begg of you to Continue to raise ore with Pumps or Engines or anything … tho' it cost £40 a tun.'*[9]

There were now unexpected developments. Mackworth and Waller both had an interest in Esgairfraith and the committee in 1700 began casting eyes on the same ground together with the West Level, where Waller claimed ore had been found. Whether the members knew anything about mining is doubtful, yet after an on-site inspection it concluded that such additions would be *'an Extraordinary advantage'*, and ordered *'an Exact Mapp'* with a report from Waller to justify the case. It arrived in 1701 or early in 1702, with a forecast estimating the ore reserves at no less than *five times* that of Esgairhir. This was confirmed by Robert Lydall, the company's Chief Operator and Smelter, and without more ado a resolution to proceed was passed.[10]

Such a course of events raises questions. In view of Mackworth's and Waller's personal interests and of the latter's sinking reputation, why were the directors so ready to take his word? Or were they all party to a share-boosting deception and wanting a scapegoat should things go wrong – a situation which actually arose with Waller's indictment a few years later. It throws a vivid light on the mystery and manoeuvring behind the scenes and, after a year or two, Esgairfaith was rarely mentioned again.

Nonetheless, by various ploys the shares held up. In July 1703, some 7,000 tons of ore (presumably undressed) were said to be on surface at Esgairhir but so chaotic were the accounts that whether or not to any profit could never be known. Then, as if not burdened enough, the company launched another and greater expansion.

## PUBLICATION OF WALLER'S *DESCRIPTION*

The book *A Description of the Mines in Cardiganshire* appeared late in 1704. It was clearly aimed to inform, or perhaps to misinform, the directors and shareholders, rather than to tempt the public at large. The preface explained that the disappointing silver returns had prompted eleven more workings to be taken on but this was mainly a pretext for opening more lead mines to replace the failing Esgairhir. Four were said each to contain the same silver (44 ozs per ton of lead), which rather suggests a figure plucked out of the air and few had any real potential at all.

The maps of the mines (see Part 2) followed the same pattern as those of 1693 and 1698, but being crude to the modern eye and difficult to interpret, have often received scant attention. However, expressing the main features in diagrammatic form was basically sound and furthermore, such an approach was novel and a revelation in the technology of mining.[11] The *Description* also

**Above:** An engraving of a pack-horse convoy in mountainous country, from Samuel Smiles' *Lives of the Engineers*. The bells were to give warning of their approach to other traffic.

**Right:** An almost identical scene today, on an ancient trackway passing through Bwlch-y-garreg ('Pass of the rocks') west of Esgairhir. The ruined barracks can just be made out in the distance. *William Bick*

sometimes contained plans of the smelting works, as if added for good measure. It is an important archive and guidance in interpretation is given later.

## THE DECLINE OF THE MINE ADVENTURE

When the expansion detailed in Waller's *Description* failed in its promise, as a last throw yet more mines were re-opened, some on the far side of Plynlimon. For a time, the gamble seemed to have paid off, for very rich copper was found at the Geufron mine west of Llanidloes[12] and the mines were soon returning profits of no less than £200 a week.[13] But Mackworth owned the leases, so where was the money going? The company had also compounded its troubles by buying the extensive business of Daniel Peck, mine owner and smelter of Flint, unaware that he was already a bankrupt. Inevitably, the financial situation became so grave that, in 1708, the directors resolved to sack all hands except those '*employed in quick work and in such as shall yield proffitt.*' Even so, two half-chests of wine were ordered for Mr Waller – economy has never begun at the top.

In 1709, Waller was made a scapegoat and sacked for incompetence. He proved a formidable opponent and rounded on Mackworth, accusing him of a variety of swindles including the Mine Adventurer's Bank, '*ridiculous in the contrivance, ignorantly began, foully carried on and scandalously ended in a labyrinth of fraud and sly, base designs*'.[14] A House of Commons enquiry then followed, in which Mackworth and others were convicted of a long series of frauds but by unforeseen circumstances, were fortunate to evade their sentences. Surprisingly, Waller redeemed himself and somehow regained his old position; the Adventurers' activities continued on a lesser scale until almost the end of the century but less is known about these later years.

Perhaps what proved the Mine Adventurers' undoing more than anything else, was the scale of operations and the unending trouble with water. Quick returns were vital and in their haste the net was cast too wide, with too many mines re-opened, plus smelting works at Garreg (now Glandyfi), near Machynlleth, which could never be justified. It is easy to forget the scale of the problems. Long before railways, cars and telephones, the horse was the fastest messenger, and goods and minerals could only go by sledge or pack-horse along ancient paths in a wild and barren landscape. Mackworth was trying to manage affairs from London or Neath; runners were employed to carry messages but at the peak of expansion, the company's twenty-eight scattered mines must have somehow worked under the loosest central control.

In retrospect, we can see that the Mine Adventure was a comedy of tragedies, especially because some of the mines eventually turned out very well. The protagonists remain intriguing, if controversial, figures: were they rogues, or visionaries whose dreams exceeded their better judgement? If Waller's promotion of 1693 was reckless, the Mine Adventure with its bogus emphasis on silver, behind which the hand of Mackworth may be sensed at every turn, was really little more than an outright fraud. He was without scruple in furthering his own interests and was commonly labelled the '*evil genius*' behind the whole concern.[15] But in the end, both became trapped in an embrace from which there could be no release. Only a closer study can bring a better understanding of this wholly remarkable concern.

## A MAN FROM THE NORTH

Waller's background has hitherto been obscure but recently more has come to light, with no doubt more to follow. Mackworth churlishly dismissed him as '*a mere miner*' but this was an injustice. Lewis Morris, the Crown mineral agent, tells us he came from Swainstone Wash, in the Forest of Stainmore in Westmorland, on the edge of bleak lead and coal country around Brough and Kirkby Stephen – a landscape not unlike much of mid-Wales. Now known as Swinestone House (below), this substantial dwelling still bears the inscription 'WW 1683' carved into the lintel over the front door. The site is ancient, with signs of considerable rebuilding.

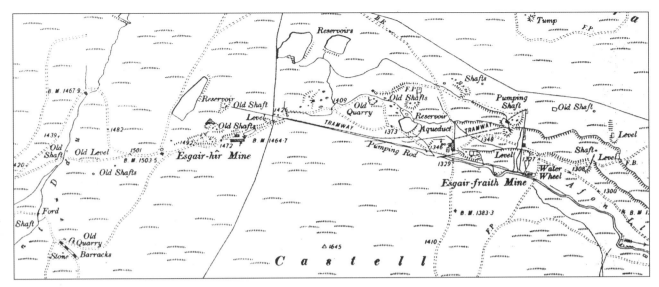

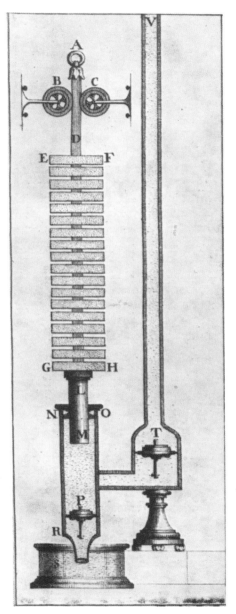

**Previous page:** Waller's home, Swinestone House, near Kirkby Stephen. The white door with 'WW 1683' on the lintel leads into a wide passage to the rear. The house has been considerably rebuilt.                                                                            *David Bick*

**Above:** Esgairhir and Esgairfraith in their final stages c.1902. During the Mine Adventure it appears that the boundary between the two ran somewhat west of the pumping shaft. Note the barracks, extreme left; the West Level began just above the ford.

**Below:** A geological map to the same scale. The bends the West Level reflect jumps from vein to vein. The long line of pumping rods dates from the 1840s.                                                                                   *O.T. Jones*, 1922

**Right:** A section through Morland's plunger pump. The weights EFGH helped to depress the plunger but needed raising again after every stroke. A hole is missing between the barrel and the outlet T.

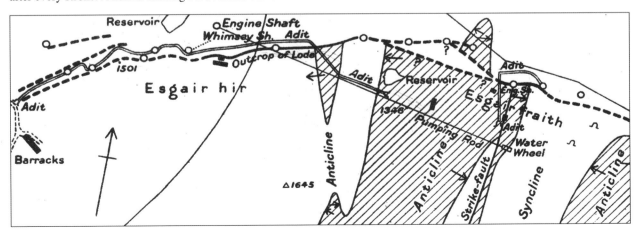

The family appears to have been of good local stock and three William Wallers were baptised at Brough between 1653 and 1657, one of whom may be our man.[16] Waller was a common name and, from 1679 to 1696, a William Waller leased the Tanhill collieries, seven miles away on the high Pennines.[17] W.J. Lewis has been less than generous about him, 'A Man of mean Circumstances, a Collier but an avaritious ambitious bad Fellow', and 'a Viper nourished in the Society's [ Mines Royal] bosom'. But to say he had 'drifted into Cardiganshire' after being forced out of the north does not square with Waller's own account.[18]

The Mine Adventurers intended to devote part of the profits to charitable purposes and, no doubt under Waller's influence, the poor of various settlements near his home in the upper Eden Valley were included – not, however, that any material benefit ensued.[19] He was said to be descended from Edmund Waller the Royalist poet (1606-87) and of Anne Waller, Sir Humphrey's grandmother. However, recent research has raised a doubt but every enquiry into the Mine Adventure brings its surprises and few could be more intriguing than this. Were the two men acquainted, or at least aware of each other, long before the legendary meeting in the Cardiganshire pub?[20]

Waller was not without education. He had a lively sense of humour, was adept with a ready phrase, and clearly possessed drive and determination in abundance. Decades later, Morris had a high opinion of his qualities as a mining engineer. He introduced the concept of time and motion study, and paid his men well but demanded a hard day's work in return. They both loved and feared him, and we get the impression of a self-made man with pretensions to rise in the social order. He drove himself hard and must have ridden thousands of miles on horseback in the course of his duties.*

Waller had two sons, Carolus (Charles), baptised on 22nd February 1695, and Georgius (George), on 21st January 1697 (1696 and 1698 by modern reckoning). His wife was Elizabeth, with Elerch given as the place of residence. It appears there was also a daughter, Faith.[21] Charles later became chief agent to the Mine Adventurers. Initially, Waller lived at 'Kavongwin' (Cefngwyn – Elerch?), and later near the Silver Mills (quite probably at Plas Mawr, beside the road in Eglwys Fach) where the schoolmaster lodged and taught his boys. As to his own fortunes the Mine Adventure turned out pretty well, for in 1709 he 'purchased an Estate lately in the north of England, and has great Sums of

Money by him …'. He may have returned there but in any case was soon back in Wales. Mackworth was still haunting him in 1721 with a Chancery case but legal documents imply he died within the year.[22]

A crumbling epitaph to the man may yet survive but in addition to his home in the Pennines, Waller's best memorials are his maps and writings, and even his publicising the memorable 'Welsh Potosi'. For in spite of the humbug behind it all, for ages the name cast a strange bewitching spell over promoters and investors alike. Buoyed by illusions of a glorious past, company after company came and went, sometimes private concerns risking their own money and all of them ending a loser.[22] Welsh Potosi, 'the richest in all Wales', was destined to linger for generations on maps of the Principality and for all those with tuppence-worth of nostalgia, there it lingers still.

## THE MINES TODAY

Physical testimony from nearly all periods can still be traced in the rugged uplands between Plynlimon and the sea, where time is slow to mark its passage. The authorities should be encouraging the heritage aspect, with its 'all the year round' appeal but nothing is done to prevent endless fly-tipping – which is a health-hazard and eyesore combined.

In addition, over the past half-century forestry and reclamation ('removing the scars of industry') have inflicted untold damage on sites which deserve protecting as much as castles or Roman antiquities. The Scheduling process might have helped but, sadly, it is more often than not a kiss of death where even the owner cannot effect repairs without a rigmarole of red tape. The approach is far too passive and merely bestows a kind of official blessing on endless neglect and decay.[23] Nonetheless, the potential is at last becoming recognised, if only in a rather leisurely and unco-ordinated fashion. Bureaucracy at best moves slowly and to take a more active role, the Welsh Mines Preservation Society was formed in 1991, so far with some very positive results.

As regards the archaeology, much still remains to be explored, because by good luck the older workings were often untouched, or too small to warrant 'improvement'. However, after so many re-openings, how to ascribe a feature of a mine to a particular period is worse than a detective story. Turning back the pages of history is a task which never ends; but for many it is the lure of the hills, the unchanging hills that beckons most of all. There, where the ghosts of Waller and legions of the 'Old Men' assemble, your spirits uplift, and no matter how many times you return, there seems always the need for going again.

---

* The wheel was scarcely known in the county, which was practically roadless. Beyond Llangurig, Lewis Morris's way to London in 1742 ran over 'immense mountains' in sight of Llanidloes and 'over commons for many miles without seeing a house anywhere near'. Thence bypassing Rhayader altogether, via Abbey Cwmhir to Kington.[24]

## NOTES ON INTERPRETATION

It is fortunate that a great wealth of primary and secondary archival material, much of it still unexplored, has survived from the Mine Adventure. This partly results from the company's vigorous promotion, and partly from the reams of self-justification spread by Waller and Mackworth when things went badly wrong. However, with all such material, we have constantly to read between the lines and the caution could not have been better expressed than by Lewis Morris when he surveyed the mines for the Crown in the 1740s:[25]

*'The reason for so many contradictions … is the different private views of each writer. Some were for leases or grants, some for augmenting their stocks in certain works and some wrote of things they knew but little or nothing of, some for putting things in the best light they could and some for concealing the truth. So that in short there is no belief in any one of them singly, but something may be gathered from them altogether.'*

The following few pages set out to assist in making the best of the various material which I have so far explored. As regards the *'Mapps'*, each was a combined plan and section, which only works with a very simple and basic approach. Also, marking the lodes as straight lines of uniform width was unrealistic. All mineral veins tend to waver and at Esgairhir, pronounced curves at surface may be seen in only a few yards.

Although tempting to dismiss at a casual glance, the maps and accompanying text contain a surprising amount as far as their limitations allow. A potential as source material is clearly there. All carry scales, which indicates a serious intent and are often quite accurate in spacial dimensions.

A difficulty often encountered is the marrying of some key feature with other evidence from the archives or on site, so that a fixed point is established; many an hour have I spent in trying to do so. At Esgairhir we are fortunate, because the two main adit portals are still readily located.

We must bear in mind that most of the mines were already old when taken up. Some had been scoured for centuries and part or all of such earlier works may have been included. At Brynpica, Waller refers to *'a Shaft sunk by the Patentees* [lessees] *of the Royal Mines'*; as for Cwmsymlog, there is no doubt that much of the development had been done before.

Taking the maps in the round, they are unique as the first mine plans to be published in this country. Their primitive nature might be thought to defer to those unable to digest anything more complex, yet, as we saw previously, they were basically to educate the directors. Presentation in this form was 'state of the art'. And how interesting to discover that on the face of it at least, the directors were no better informed than the public itself.

In addition, there is sometimes the suspicion that obscurity and poor correlation with other evidence was sometimes intentional, to avoid becoming a hostage to fortune. It may be so and certainly the maps do not compare to those of Lewis Morris, compiled with a more altruistic purpose in mind. But we must be thankful they were made at all.

A detail from Kitchin's map of 1777 showing Welsh Potosi. In 1854 George Borrow tramped the road, little more than a rough track, south from Machynlleth past the mine on his way to Ponterwyd. The A 44 westwards from 'Pont Hernid' to Aberystwyth did not then exist. 'Gesten Tu' is presumably Ystumtuen – yet another variation in spelling.

## ESGAIRHIR AND THE MAPS

> *'Pray,' said I, 'what company is this, the directors of which are so solicitous about the safety of strangers'. 'The Potosi Mining Company,' said he, 'the richest in all Wales.'*
>
> George Borrow, *Wild Wales*

### THE 1693 MAP (right)

This scarcely-known map is the first and best of the four. The vertical scale differs by a factor of four from the horizontal, thus greatly exaggerating the surface gradients.

The leased ground ran eastwards from the original shaft (B) for 1,200 yards into the hillside of Esgair-fraith, marked by the letter N on the north vein – '*vaine 1*'. This distance agrees with the scale and the depth of shaft B, quoted as 52 yards, is again about right. A study makes it clear that the great discovery and its aftermath, B, C, D and E, were made just north of the road where it crosses the ridge (see page 20).

H-I, described as a natural outbreak of the vein, may coincide with a massive outcrop of quartz between the forestry road and the old road on its north side, just east of the gate into the woodland. The West Level is shown reaching shaft B but this was merely a declaration of intent – it had probably not even begun. The proposed East Level M seems a needless expense, unless to work the vast quantities of ore presumed to be there.

The vertical section is broadly correct but as to the plan view depicting the lodes, here we are not so sure. As aerial photographs show, the fault fracture of ore-bearing ground was very wide. The plan scales 28 yards separating veins 1 and 6, which may be so, but with the lack of exposures or detailed plans we cannot be sure. Within its limitations it seems a pretty honest record.

### THE 1698 MAP

This version, from *An Essay on the Value of the Mines …*', (largely the work of Mackworth), not only included silver but also copper. The map is perfunctory and strangely short on detail, suggesting little activity in the meantime. The sett or leased ground scales little more than 1,000 yards long, not the true 1,200 and the overall width of the veins has increased from 28 to 45 yards. The copper veins i and h were of little or no account and simply added for good measure. (They presumably correspond to branches off the main lode as shown on the geological map, page 11.)

**Right:** Waller's 1693 map of Esgairhir. *British Library*

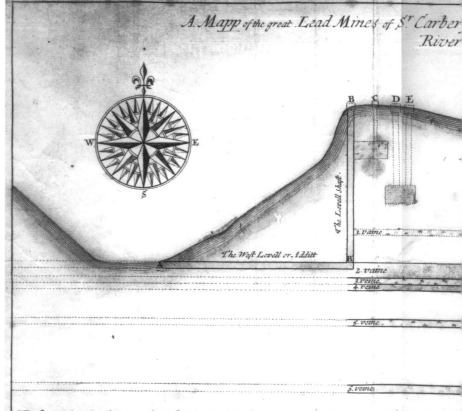

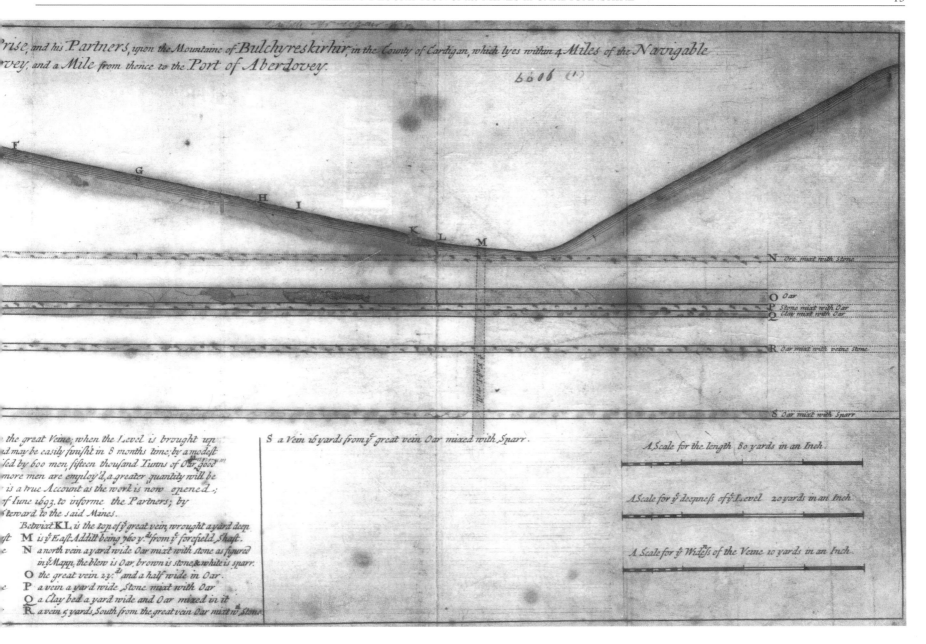

rise, and his *Partners*, upon the Mountaine of *Bulchyreskirhir*, in the County of Cardigan, which lyes within 4 *Miles* of the *Navigable* vey, and a *Mile* from thence to the *Port of Aberdovey*.

N   Ore mixt with stone

O   Oar
P   Stone mixt with Oar
Q   Clay mixt with Oar

R   Oar mixt with veine stone

S   Oar mixt with Sparr

S   a Vein 16 yards from y great vein Oar mixed with Sparr.

the great Veine, when the Level is brought up
d may be easily finisht in 8 months time; by a modest
ed by 600 men, fifteen thousand Turns of Oar good
more men are employ'd, a greater quantity will be
is a true Account as the work is now opened;
f June 1693. to informe the Partners; by
teward to the said Mines.

   Betwixt K L, is the top of y great vein, wrought a yard deep.
   M   is y East Addilt being 760 y.d from y forefield Shaft.
   N   a north vein a yard wide Oar mixt with stone as figured
      in y Mapp, the blew is Oar, brown is stone, & white is sparr.
   O   the great vein 2 y.d and a half wide in Oar.
   P   a vein a yard wide Stone mixt with Oar
   Q   a Clay bed a yard wide and Oar mixed in it
   R   a vein 5 yards South from the great vein Oar mixt w. Stone

A Scale for the length 80 yards in an Inch.

A Scale for y deepnefs of y Level 20 yards in an Inch.

A Scale for y Widefs of the Veine 10 yards in an Inch.

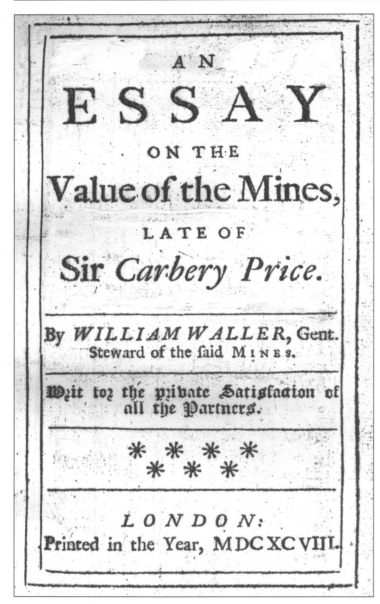

The title page from Waller's *Essay*, 1698.

## THE 1701 'GHOST' MAP

In the latter half of 1701, Waller was instructed to prepare '*A Map of the Mines of Esgirhyr and Esgirhyr ffraeth Showing the height of the Mountaine the boundaryes of the Old and new Liberty and the deepnesse of the Severall Levells.*'[26]

This was part of the grand design to acquire more land at both ends of the existing operation. Unfortunately, the map has not survived; however, from his description it was identical to the 1698 version, extended eastwards to include Esgairfraith, right over the hills to the river beyond. The additions were as follows:

*From M to the End of the Hill and down to N is Eskyrfraith Liberty being 1150 yards in length … and 124 yards deep …*

*N is Eskyrfraith Level at 124 yards deep which is 60* yards *deeper than the present Levell.* [Esgairhir?]

*O is Eskyrhyr Levell at 64 yards deep.* [The West Level on the 1698 map.]

*P is a little Brooke that runns att the Bottome of the Hill.*

Waller went on to explain that from the '*two Veines more that Crosses the ground on the South side of the Mountaine I have raised Oar in both the One Copper and the other Lead.*'

He continued:□*The Levell or Auditt to Eskyrfraeth will be 124 yards deep being 55 yards the deeper levell and 5 yards the higher mountaine*', a statement which might have been better expressed. However, to claim that the adit was 55 yards below the Esgairhir level (if that is what he meant) was stretching the truth. Near Lluest-grafia (SN 751913) is an old level in the right area for N but whether actually connected with Waller is hard to tell. Ostensibly, upon such recommendations did the company go ahead with acquisitions which were to avail it little or nothing in return.

## THE 1704 MAP

The final version is well known from Waller's *Description*. The lease now included the West Level and east of shaft B again measures 1,000 yards. However, this now appears correct since it only reaches the East Level and omits Esgairfraith. The veins have now been reduced to a more realistic number but with no indication of their width. Copper, which Mackworth afterwards admitted never made a farthing profit, is no longer mentioned. P, the site of Welsh Potosi, may coincide with the ruins of later barracks near the West Level entrance.

Whenever possible, the three maps should be studied along with other material. As an example, the company Minutes for 1700-1 refer to shaft H going down in the '*bog work*' to meet the arrival of East Level. Short of a further plan, now lost, at this date H could only refer to the 1693 map. H is also identified with the '*Bog-Work*' on the map of 1704. From other abstracts, it probably equated with Shaft Isaf (Lower Shaft, east of modern cattle sheds) on a section reproduced on page 20. Thus we can glimpse the enigmas as well as the light that such records throw on these historic sites.

The Select Committee continued to badger Waller about the West Level but we may suspect that he knew the unspeakable truth, that Sir Carbery's cupboard, so beckoning and bountiful at first, was already ransacked and its inner recesses were bare. In fact the level had already been switched to a south lode, ignoring the original discovery altogether.[27] Nonetheless, two plunger pumps invented by Sir Samuel Morland were ordered, perhaps as a public relations exercise, and Isaak Thompson the maker was urged to come down from London to install them.[28] Whether the machinery ever arrived is unclear. Perhaps, like other old pumping gear, it lies rusting and forgotten in some flooded gallery, its scrap value not worth the cost of recovery. It is unlikely; it is too much to hope for, even supposing the workings might still be accessible but you can never be sure.

**Above:** The 1840s barracks, looking north-west, and quite probably the site of the 1690s *Welsh Potosi*. The trackway running from right to left just beyond is the old road to Talybont. The white spot marks Bwlch-y-garreg pass.                    *William Bick*
**Right:** Waller's map of 1698, from his *Essay*.

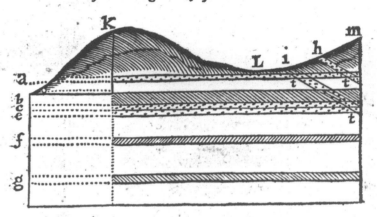

A DESCRIPTION *of the Silver, Lead and Copper-mines, late of Sir* Carbery Price, *lying in* Cardiganshire, *within four Miles of the Navigable River* Dovey, *and from thence a Mile by Water to the Port of Aberdovey, where Vessels of three or four hundred Tuns may ride with great Safety.*

*a* The North Vein of Lead-oar, three Foot wide.
*b* The great Lead-vein, eleven Foot wide.
*c* A Vein of Lead-oar six Foot wide.
*e* A Vein of Lead-oar three Foot wide.
*f* A Vein of Green Copper-oar, four Foot wide, and yields three Tun of Copper from twenty Tun of Oar.
*g* The Bog-vein, four Foot wide, all Potter's Oar.
*h* The Cross Vein of Lead-oar, three Foot wide.

*i* The Cross Vein of Brown Copper-oar, five Foot wide, and yields five Tun of Copper out of twenty Tun of Oar
*k* The first great Shaft and Western Boundary.
*l* The East Level.
*m* The Eastern Boundary.
*t t t* The places where the Cross Veins meet with the other Veins; which are called by Miners, the (T) of the Veins, and are accounted the richest part of them.
*o* The West Level.

Note, *All the said Veins are fix'd and settled betwixt firm and solid Sides, and rise equally near to the Surface of the Ground; and all (except the Cross Veins) lye parallel to the great Vein, descending downwards like the Mine of* Potozi; *but being many in Number, and crossing each other could not be better described together on Paper.*
The Scale for the Length four hundred Yards in an Inch; and for the Height of the Mountain eighty Yards in an Inch; and for the Distance between the Veins forty Yards in an Inch.

# THE
## FOURTH ABSTRACT
### Of the State of the
## MINES of *Bwlchyr Eskir-hir*,
### IN THE
## County of Cardigan:

From the 10th Day of *December* last ( inclusive )
to this present 5th Day of May, 1701.

### By Order of the Committee.

THE Committee, since their last printed Account of the Mines, have receiv'd several Letters from Mr. *Waller*, and others, to the effect following, *viz.*

#### December the 10th. from Mr. *Waller*.

That on *Sunday* last he arriv'd at the Mines, from his Northern Journey, and found the Bargains and Works in good order.

The Bog-work continues in good Oar: we are crossing there from the Shaft K to h, and we are sinking a Shaft in the Oar, at H, to meet it. The new Work mends downward, and is much improv'd since I left it. We continue sinking in Oar at E, and the West Level goes well forward.

We are raising Oar in the ends of the great Work, but cannot reach the Sole for Water, being we cannot get the large Engine to draw Water.

We have the Timber upon the Cupulo at *Garrick*, and wall'd the Flews eight foot high. The new Key is wall'd, and we are filling it up to the Level of the Cupulo. I hope to have Fifty or Sixty Men soon after *Christmas*, they having promis'd to come as soon as they have receiv'd their *Christmas* Pay.

#### December 11. from Mr. *Tho. Hawkins*, at Neath.

That the Smelting and Refining at *Neath* goes well forward; and that he had sent by Mr. *Tanner*, the *Monmouth* Carrier, One thousand Sixty seven Ounces, Seventeen Pennyweight, Seven grains, of Bullion; together with his Accounts.

#### December 17. from Mr. *Waller*.

The Shaft at H, in the Bog-work, goes down in fine firm Potters-Oar, and widens as we go.

The New-work is much wider in Oar than when Mr. *Minshall* saw it, and the Oar there seems to be the same with that in the Bog-work.

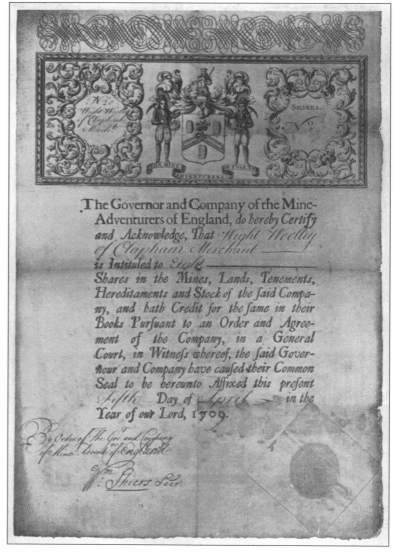

**Above:** Money sunk and lost. A Mine Adventurers' share certificate issued in 1709 by William Shiers the secretary, to Wight Woolley, merchant of Clapham.
**Left:** Abstract from an Abstract. Note the references to the cupola at 'Garrick' and to silver bullion from Neath

**Left:** Ancient opencuts at Esgairhir 30 years ago, now filled with rubbish, showing a sharp curve in the lode. Shaft Moses was somewhere here. The ruined building held a 19th century steam engine. *Richard Bird*

**Top left:** A row of trial shafts, like bomb craters, on a south lode at Esgairhir, looking west. *David Bick*

**Above:** The portal to the East level is now almost lost in undergrowth. *David Bick*

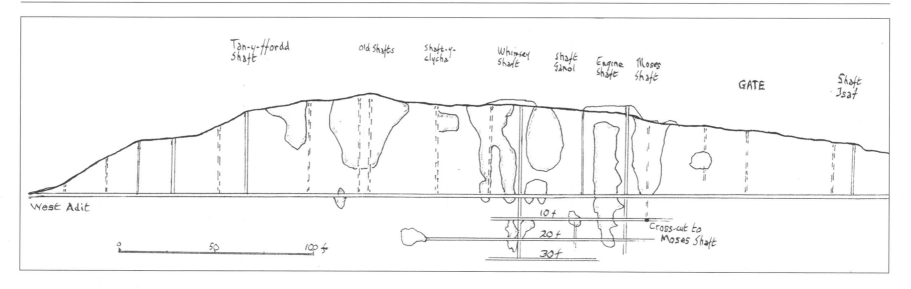

**Above:** This section, drawn in 1947 and showing the shafts and stoped parts of the lodes, was based on a much older plan, R 140a. The vertical scales below and above adit are inconsistent and the levels have clearly been added later. Note that the orebody at Shaft B etc. ('Old Shafts') had faded out above the adit, which in fact bypassed it altogether. 'GATE' indicates the gate into the forestry area.

**Left:** An ancient stone-lined shaft near the old road to Machynlleth.   *David Bick*

**An aerial photograph of Esgairhir, 1992**    *Crown copyright: RCAHMW*

A   1840 road from Talybont
B   West Level
C   Adit (see photograph below)
D   Barracks
E   17th Century Shafts
F   Leats
G   Shaft B (p.14)
H   Old road to Machynlleth
I   Trials on a south lode
J   Whimsey Shaft

K   1870s enginehouse
L   Engine Shaft
M   Flat-rod trenches
N   Old Mine Road
O   Forestry Road
P   Mine Offices
Q   Opencuts and Shaft Moses
R   1840s Tramway
S   Gate into Forestry

The run-in adit heading towards shaft G on the skyline, possibly pre-Waller.
*David Bick*

## THE OTHER MINES

All the remaining mines in the *Description* were worked under leases acquired by Mackworth and later assigned to the company. From Sir John Pettus's *Fodinae Regales*, it appears that before Myddelton took over the Crown lease in 1617, the *'five great Works'* for silver were *'the Darren Hills, Coomfumblock, Coommervin, Coginian* [Goginan] *and Talybont.'*

At this point it is worth recalling that according to Pettus, Myddelton lost all his wealth in bringing the 'New River' to London but in fact the leat was completed before he came to Wales, not afterwards. This basic blunder has been endlessly repeated and like all such over a period of time, an error in print becomes so accepted that to doubt it is almost a heresy and to erase it, almost impossible. But it serves as a reminder to check the source whenever possible, a tedious business though it is.[29]

Ancient opencuts and sundry workings on the Havan lode. Note the tramway incline ascending in the foreground. Waller's activities were in this vicinity.                         *William Bick*

### Bwlch Caninog, Grid ref. SN 725879 (page 34)

Near the source of the Afon Cyneiniog east of Talybont, the Plynlimon & Hafan Tramway, to give access to a quarry, ascended a long and steep incline in the 1890s, occupying a wide rift at the head of the valley.[30] In the same rift, two lodes outcrop 20 or 30 yards apart and parallel to the incline. Sundry workings extend all the way up. O.T. Jones recorded five adits and there are deep opencuts where the sheer quantity of fallen rocks impute a great antiquity.

Constructing the incline robbed the dumps of much material and also buried some of the workings. The tips mainly comprise a dark brown mineral, which some suppose is siderite (sparry iron-ore) and others, ankerite. It stands out as massive ribs in the lode and in mid-Wales is a harbinger of copper, which also occurs here.

Hand-cobbed waste is evident in several places and two stone-arched adits near the foot of the incline might originate from the Mine Adventure. The mine was later known as Hafan or Havan.

### Cwmsymlog, Grid ref. SN 696837 – 704838 (page 36)

Cwmsymlog was very productive well before Myddelton, and graphic accounts of the perilous state of the workings have survived.[31]

In view of its glowing record, Waller's hopes ran high and, on 21st January 1706, he sent to Mackworth *'a Piece of our Glorious Ore, got in the middle Level … being now above a Yard wide; I doubt not but we will have some thousand of Tons from this vein …'*. And in May 1707, in a level under the old stopes was *'2 Foot four Inches in fine solid Ore'* in three ribs with veinstone between. But in spite of many more reports in similar style, the great bonanza somehow never quite materialised.

In a very interesting account of 13th January 1707, Waller mentioned that the *'low Level is Hard, and I want yet 15 Fathom to come to Sir H. Middleton upper Engin Pit.'* Therefore, unless clearing a fall, they were driving Bushell's adit forward, although on page 36 the evidence suggests that before this time it was already further east – a typical conundrum. The engine pit was about where the Cwmsymlog stream crosses the lode.[32]

**Goginan**, Grid ref. SN 691818 (page 38)

Scarcely less renowned for its silver than Cwmsymlog, Goginan was also wrought by Myddelton and to great advantage by Bushell. The geography made it ideal for working by adits and the deep drainage level, which emerges next to a bridge over the stream, has been attributed to Bushell. Its cut-and-cover construction to gain every inch of depth has a strong resemblance to Cwmerfin (SN 697828), which is not part of the present account.[33]

As elsewhere, Waller was obliged to substitute rhetoric for ore. Most of his reports were playing for time, barely intelligible and akin to a drunken ramble, at least until a map (now lost) was compiled late in 1705.[34] Here is a letter to Sir Thomas Mackworth, 17th March 1706:

*'Your Mrs Goginian, is much improved … , if I had a Sump down at the surface of the Stoops, and a Drift 11 Yards long to it, I could then sink my Shaft and work in my Apple Forehead, which at present I am watered from; but I shall not be long so, being 22 yards under it'*

Waller was unlucky, since in the 1840s Goginan became one of the best mines ever worked in Cardiganshire.

**Brynpica**, Grid ref. SN 697822 (page 40)

This was an old work north-east of Goginan, and Waller's endeavours involved a long level and several shafts. Nothing more than endless promises resulted.

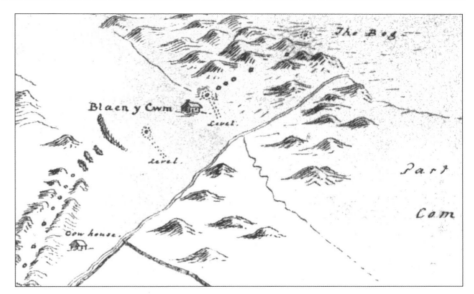

Above: A detail from Morris's plan showing two levels. The diagonal boundary line passing near Blaen y Cwm is probably M in the lower drawing. *NLW*

Below: An artist's fanciful impression of Cwmsymlog in *Fodinae Regales*, 1670.

## COMSUMLOCK HILL.

A 1,2,3,4. The old Works of Sir *Hugh Middleton* and Mr. *Bushell*.
B to B The Round Holes signifie the Shafts of the Mine.
C The Windlace to wind up Oar out of the Shafts.
D A New Vein.
E Sir *Hugh Middleton's* Adit which carried but that Level.
F The New Adit which carries on the Great Level now working.
G Mr. *Dickinsons* and Mr. *Hills* Adit to drein the Castle Works.
H Sir *Hugh Middleton's* decayed Chappel.
I The old Stamping House.
K The Smelting Mills, to be supposed six miles from the Hill.
L A great Space of Ground not yet wrought.

M The Brook that divides the Hill.
N The Stream which drives the Mills.

**Above:** After landscaping, all that remains of Cwmervin (Bwlch) is this unworthy re-build of the adit entrance.          *David Bick*

**Right:** An aerial view in 1992 of Pencraigddu – P; ancient trials – T; Cwmarvin – C (A is the adit);  Brynpica – B. The lode outcrop runs near to, or within the forestry.          *Crown Copyright, RCAHMW*

### Cwmervin *(Bwlch)*, Grid ref. SN 703823 (page 42)

Myddelton worked this mine, which was also known as Bwlch Cwmerfin or simply Bwlch. It is distinct from the mine to the north-west, Cwmerfin Fach, also named Cwmerfin in the 19th century.

Where the Goginan lode reaches the summit separating the next valley, the north branch splits again, giving rise to parallel workings. In April 1707, Waller reported '*Bwlch Comervin Level goes on well … the Workmen think they hear the water beat in the Vein; but he fears its too far off yet; for by his Dialling of it, wants about 8 Fathom.*' The vein was perhaps the Goginan main lode to the south but in any event the outcome was unproductive.

### Pencraigddu, Grid ref. SN711824 (page 44)

In 1701, Mackworth inspected a vein at '*Pencraigethee*', said to be rich in silver and wrought by a level 14 yards deep, but '*afterwards left for want of a deeper Levell.*' On the strength of this, the Adventurers began or extended such a level along the lode from a crosscut known as Level Reich or Level yr Uch, aimed at some very old workings just within the present forestry, to which an ancient leat can still be traced.[39] Grassy tips mark the course of the lode, which splits as it approaches the mine. Whether the level was ever finished seems unlikely, for a shorter adit, the Llettymarallt, was driven later almost as deep from the east.

Lewis Morris relates that the Mine Adventurers '*fell in upon a great body of ore … a very rich steel grain'd silver ore*' and they were still at work there in 1744. He rated the prospects very highly but it was never properly tried in depth.

### Ystumtuen, Grid ref. SN 733788 (page 46)

At the end of 1698, Mackworth leased from William Powel of Nanteos the mines of Ystumtuen and Cwmystwyth. Both were old works of lead rather than silver and many miles from Garreg.

**Above:** Ancient trial workings on the lode outcrop looking east towards Pencraigddu, past *Bwlchrhennaid* shaft, now capped, in the middle distance.      *David Bick*

**Below:** Shafts at Pencraigddu, looking west. The footway shaft is enclosed in an ugly steel fence. Note the stone horse-whim pedestal bearing for the shaft in the foreground.      *David Bick*

| Names of the Mines. | Numb. of Fath. driven, sunk & sumped. | Quantity of Oar brought from every Mine. | | | Total expend. in driving, raising and dressing. | | |
|---|---|---|---|---|---|---|---|
| | Fathom. | Tuns | C | Q | l. | s. | d. |
| Bwlchyr-Eskir-Hyr | 394 | 1111 | 07 | | 1240 | 11 | 01½ |
| Coninogg | 383 | 266 | 09 | | 0610 | 11 | |
| Cumsumlocke | 840 | 035 | 05 | | 1099 | 16 | 10 |
| Goginan | 633 | 020 | 16 | 02 | 0627 | 10 | 03 |
| Brinpickay | 265 | | | | 0239 | 11 | |
| Cumarvin | 164 | | | | 0231 | 09 | |
| Pencraigddy | 325 | 13 | 5 | 03 | 0277 | 18 | 03¼ |
| Cyland | 131 | | | | 0066 | 02 | 04 |
| Dole Rhyland | 121 | | | | 0085 | 01 | 11 |
| Eskyr-fraith | 110 | | | | 0123 | 05 | |
| Estimtean | 349 | 594 | 6 | | 1141 | 15 | 10¼ |
| Cumustwith | 051 | 580 | 18 | C1 | 1173 | 10 | 10¼ |
| Nantrevach | 061 | | | | 0043 | 05 | 02 |
| Penrevach | 110 | | | | 0092 | 04 | 10 |
| Silver-Hill | 189 | | | | 0224 | 10 | 05¼ |
| Stamping-mill-veine | 128 | | | | 0167 | 03 | 00½ |
| West-craigy-moyne | 026 | | | | 0006 | 04 | 01½ |
| Brunont | 042 | | | | 0013 | 09 | |
| Bulchyrenald | 021 | | | | 0031 | 13 | 09 |
| Nantmellin | 088 | | | | 0085 | 16 | 09 |
| Brintile | 200 | | | | 0108 | 08 | 00½ |
| Gayre | 021 | 3 | 02 | | 0022 | 09 | 05 |
| Siglanlace | 057 | | | | 0042 | 14 | 08 |
| Copermine at Gyfren | 236 | | 14 | | 0108 | 06 | 10 |
| Maysmoore | 004 | 4 | 04 | | 0017 | 17 | 10 |
| Total | | 2630 | 07 | 02 | 7881 | 17 | 04 |

The table shows Waller's record of work done and ore raised in the 4½ years up to August 1708. Ostensibly, the results were very disappointing but in several instances we may suspect that the whole truth was not being told. The six mines after 'Cumustwith' are all in the vicinity. 'Dole Rhyland' is Eaglebrook and 'Gayre' is Aberdaunant. Simon Hughes reports that Maysmoore is in the Lyfnant Valley, south-east of Cefn Maesmawr.

On 7th September 1705, two Derbyshire miners went down a shaft at 'Estimtyen', where either side of a rider 'was a Rib of good Ore, about a Foot thick; we saw the Ore bare a considerable length; the Miners are working in several Stoops, and there is a fair Streak of Ground before the Vein.'

In May 1707, Waller reported over 120 tons of dressed ore ready for carriage and a few days later 'that he had received 4 half Chests of Wine; that he had hoped to see some of the Company this Summer … and drink Success to the Mines.'

Ystumtuen was on the whole profitable and the Adventurers held it for many years; Morris later described it in some detail.[40]

### Cwmystwyth, Grid ref. SN  800745 – 811756 (page 48)

The extensive nature of this celebrated mine, where no less than 30 lodes and 84 surface features (shafts, adits and stopes) have been identified, render it the ultimate challenge for the mining historian and archaeologist.[35] It had

Opencuts at Ystumtuen, 2003, looking east along the lode. Countless such historic features have long served as rubbish-tips and the abuse continues. *William Bick*

long been worked when Waller paid a visit in 1691 and he was active there in 1698, under a lease granted to Mackworth in which seven different workings were itemised.

In 1704, the *Description* implies that the Adventurers were active near the stamping mill, remains of which still survive on the east bank of Nant yr Onnen. But the operations get no mention in a report of 7th September 1705 stating '*there is an old Work called Beltazer's Work, which has been very large, and there is now a Rib of Ore a Foot thick … The Men are raising Ore in several Shafts … There is a new Work and several hopeful Tryals in that mountain.*'

However, the stamping mill level is probably one of those mentioned later. The company had various trials in hand and how to identify them with present-day remains is prompting much enquiry and investigation.

In his typical enigmatic style, in April 1707 Waller describes an unknown site where '*Mr Jackson's Mrs is hard, that he finds the Shaft he is sinking, and the Vein is not the same, … for he cannot find the Vein heads so much as the Shaft is distant, that the Ore Mr Jackson saw there, is now increased, to 5 Foot wide firm Ore …*'.[36] I have no ideas as to the relevance of the late Mr & Mrs Jackson.

The total amount of production from Cwmystwyth under the Mine Adventurers is uncertain but, as at Geufron, there lingers the feeling that not all of it went through the company's books.

A detail from W.W. Smyth's 1846 map of Cwmystwyth. The stamps were near Bonsall's Level (top), with Waller's Nantrefach Level lower down on the left (see pages 48-50).

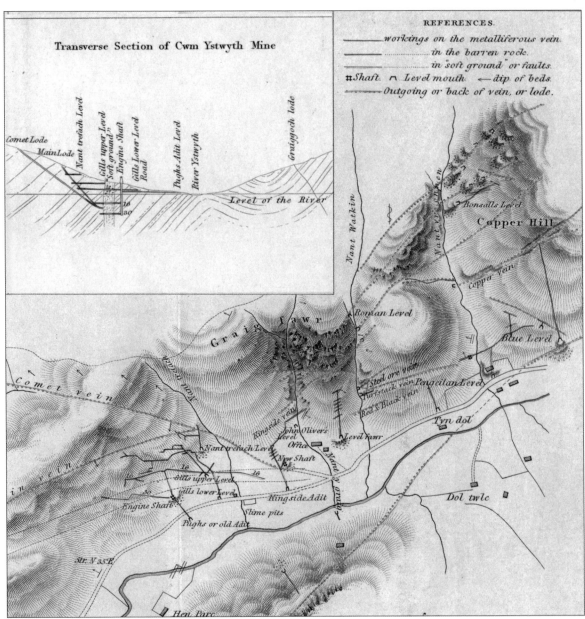

**Above:** These crumbling ruins are without doubt the remnants of Waller's stamping mill, high in Nant-yr- onnen. The author is standing where the combined wheel and stamp-axle passed through a slot in the wall to work the stamps on the far side. The rough transverse wall in front of the slot was added for no obvious purpose, after the wheel had been removed. The water for the wheel came from a launder above the stone pier on the left. Measurements suggest the diameter was about 12 ft. In 1788, the Derbyshire engineer Francis Thompson gave a valuable and detailed account of a mill at '*Mr Bonsall's Mine*'. It was clearly the old one in use, with three stamps as before. Each operated four times per revolution and weighed about 8 stone (1 cwt. or 50 kg) with a drop of 12 inches. The machine was very effective – '*One man and a boy do more business than 20 women.*[32] It is a sobering thought that in the miraculous creation of mineral lodes, nature is the first and greatest concentrator, only for man to dissipate her bounty beyond all hope of recovery.                          *William Bick*

**Right:** A drawing of a rough-and-ready 19th century four-head stamp mill at Polgooth, in Cornwall. Sometimes they were housed within a building, sometimes not; which applied to Waller's mill is uncertain.                          Samuel Smiles, *Lives of the Engineers*

# PART 2

## Waller's A DESCRIPTION of the MINES in CARDIGANSHIRE

### BIBLIOGRAPHICAL NOTES

The book's history is by no means straightforward, with opinions as to the date of publication ranging from 1692 to 1709. The British Library has ascribed it to 1704. Thus far, I have traced a dozen copies of which only my own, acquired many years ago from a dealer, is in private hands. The individual maps of the mines were first mentioned by the Select Committee early in October 1704, when Waller was *'desired to perfect the mapps brought up by him and that he Enquire into the Charge of putting the same on copper plates …'*.

As to the key map (overleaf), nothing has come to light about its origins. Was it based on something earlier, or drawn from scratch? In parts it is badly astray, Ystumtuen (*'Istimtean'*) being much too far north and the scale is economical. For instance, Ystumtuen – Garregg measures barely 9 miles as the crow flies, whereas the truth is 11$^1$/$_2$. The plate dimensions, 17 x 13 inches, were unwieldy for the page size, requiring multiple folding and inspection suggests that some books were issued with the map omitted. Perhaps it was also available separately. The ten individual maps of the mines were folded twice to fit the book and the crease marks are clearly visible on each.

The *Description* probably left the press soon after November 1704, when it was ordered that *'the settling of the preamble to Mr Waller's book of Mapps be referred to Sir Humphrey Mackworth and Mr Breton and they be desired to amend the same.'* This is presumably referring to the preamble which begins:

*'Honour'd SIRS,*

*It is not for the Vanity of appearing in Print that I give you this Second Trouble …'* (The first was presumably the Essay of 1698, which as we have seen, was mainly the work of Mackworth).

The form of address suggests that Waller's intended audience was the directors and shareholders. However, here a peculiar mystery attends, for in one copy at least the preamble is replaced by a page having just the bare title (see page 31), without even the date and author's name. But it does contain all four plans, which may be a clue.

Thus the book appeared in two editions but which came first, or were they concurrent and was the title-paged version meant for the general public? As an interesting aside, this general absence in surviving copies of a title page has had some quite unexpected and even amusing consequences. It has long presented difficulties for the serious student but not for Robert Hunt, who solved the problem by the novelty of concocting not one but *two* entirely spurious titles to fill the gap. Here are a couple of footnotes from the same page of his 1848 Memoir, of which the least said, the better:

W. Waller, *Report on the Cardiganshire Mines*
Mr Waller's *Account of the Mines of Cardiganshire*

Who would suppose that these phantom references were both pseudonyms for Waller's *Description*? They have perplexed authors ever since, enduring in bibliography to the present day; and knowing the power of the printed word, are no doubt destined to continue to do so.

As for the plates of the works, most of the above survivors have none and only a National Library of Wales copy has four (reproduced to a smaller scale, pages 52-58). The varying plate sizes suggest they were not drawn up specifically for use in the book but already existed for another purpose. This may explain why *'Garrigg Furnices'* shows signs of cropping at the top.

In addition, whilst the plans of the three Cardiganshire smelting works are clearly by the same hand and probably drawn up locally, the *'Workhouse at Neath'* is different. The standard is higher and much more detailed. There are hints of an earlier plan extended but in any case we may suspect it originated at Neath. As to Waller's *Description* in general, all sorts of intriguing questions arise, which will never be solved.

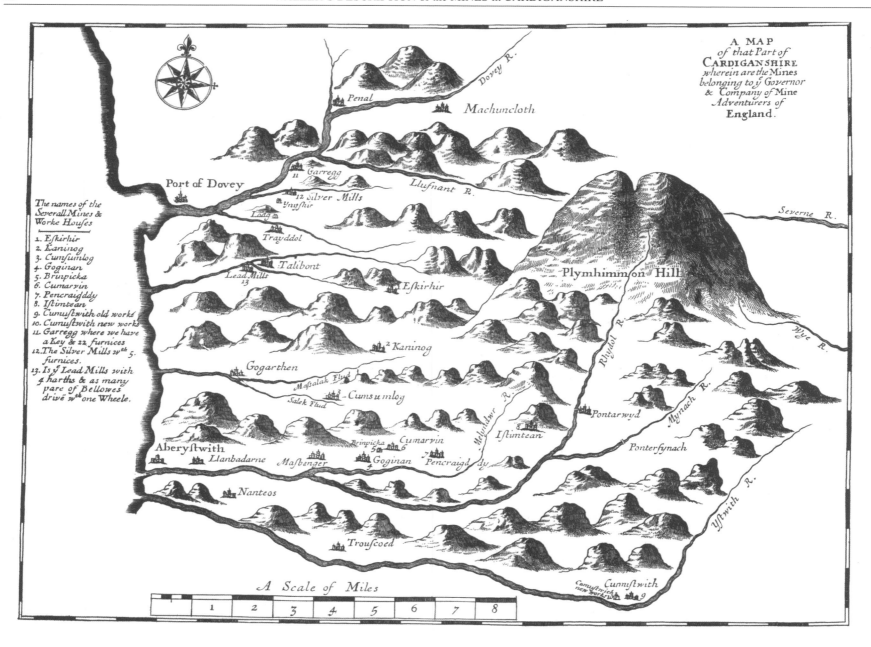

The names of the
Severall Mines &
Worke Houses

1. Eskirhir
2. Kaninog
3. Cumsumlog
4. Goginan
5. Brinpicka
6. Cumarvin
7. Pencraigddy
8. Istimtean
9. Cumustwith old works
10. Cumustwith new works
11. Garregg where we have
    a Key & 22 furnices
12. The Silver Mills wth 5.
    furnices.
13. Is ye Lead Mills with
    4 harths & as many
    pare of Bellowes
    drive wth one Wheele.

A MAP
of that Part of
CARDIGANSHIRE
wherein are the Mines
belonging to ye Governor
& Company of Mine
Adventurers of
England.

A Scale of Miles

| 1 | 2 | 3 | 4 | 5 | 6 | 7 | 8 |

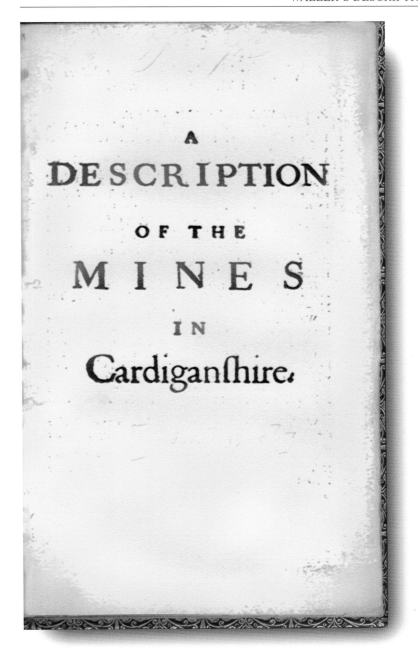

A

# DESCRIPTION

## OF THE

# MINES

## IN

# Cardiganshire.

[ I ]

Honour'd SIRS,

IT is not for the Vanity of appearing in Print, that I give you this Second Trouble, but to give you the prefent State of the Mines. In 1698. I wrote an Effay for the Information of the then Partners; wherein I promifed to raife Ore at Eskirhir, at 14 s. 3 d. per Tun; and fince I have raifed fome Thoufands of Tuns at 3 s. 7 d. per Tun, including Wafhing and making Merchantable, which is a much lefs Price than what I then propofed: But finding that Eskirhir Ore did not bear that Quantity in Silver that other Mines in the Country did, which being not underftood, lay unwrought; and the Nation being engaged in an expenfive War, and wanting Bullion, we ventured upon the Working of thefe Mines, as not doubting but they will turn to a National Advantage, as well as a confiderable Profit to our felves; and you will find by the following Maps, that I have managed Eleven Levels, or Addits, befides thofe in Eskirhir, which have all been as a dead Charge upon us for fome Years, but now the moft of them will yield us good Profit. Thefe Things being confider'd, with the Charge of your Smelting Furnaces, Refining Furnaces, and Red-Lead Mills, I hope it will be no ftrange Thing to you, why we have not yet made a Dividend of more than 6 l. per Cent, per Ann.    I am,

Honour'd SIRS,

Your moft Obedient Servant,

W. WALLER.

## ESGAIRHIR

The plan and description have been discussed on pages 16-17. It is strange that C was now to be drained from the East Level, rather than the West Level, so long in the driving. The Mountain E may be the knoll near I, page 21.

The lack of much new information and the addition of 'padding' reflects the general decline of activity by 1704.

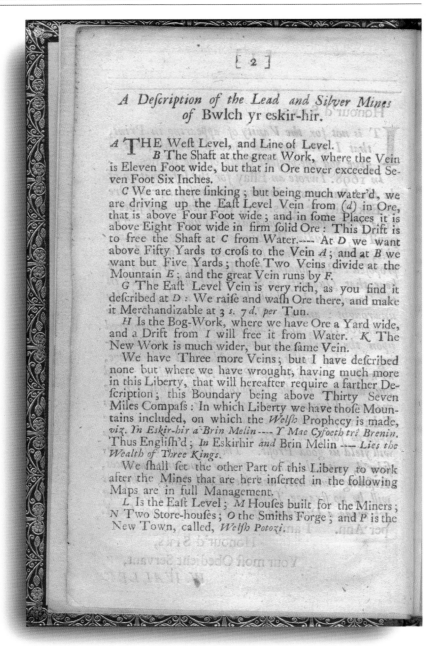

*A Description of the Lead and Silver Mines of Bwlch yr eskir-hir.*

A THE West Level, and Line of Level.

B The Shaft at the great Work, where the Vein is Eleven Foot wide, but that in Ore never exceeded Seven Foot Six Inches.

C We are there sinking; but being much water'd, we are driving up the East Level Vein from (d) in Ore, that is above Four Foot wide; and in some Places it is above Eight Foot wide in firm solid Ore: This Drift is to free the Shaft at C from Water.—— At D we want above Fifty Yards to cross to the Vein A; and at B we want but Five Yards; those Two Veins divide at the Mountain E; and the great Vein runs by F.

G The East Level Vein is very rich, as you find it described at D: We raise and wash Ore there, and make it Merchandizable at 3 s. 7 d. per Tun.

H Is the Bog-Work, where we have Ore a Yard wide, and a Drift from I will free it from Water. K The New Work is much wider, but the same Vein.

We have Three more Veins; but I have described none but where we have wrought, having much more in this Liberty, that will hereafter require a farther Description; this Boundary being above Thirty Seven Miles Compass: In which Liberty we have those Mountains included, on which the *Welsh* Prophecy is made, viz. *In Eskir-hir a Brin Melin ---- Y Mac Cyfoeth tre Brenin.* Thus English'd; *In Eskirhir and Brin Melin ---- Lies the Wealth of Three Kings.*

We shall set the other Part of this Liberty to work after the Mines that are here inserted in the following Maps are in full Management.

L Is the East Level; M Houses built for the Miners; N Two Store-houses; O the Smiths Forge; and P is the New Town, called, *Welsh Potozi.*

**Previous page:** The alternative 'title pages' to Waller's *Description*.
**Above:** Heading uphill from the West Level past old surface workings to the 'great Work' on the horizon.
           *Simon Hughes*

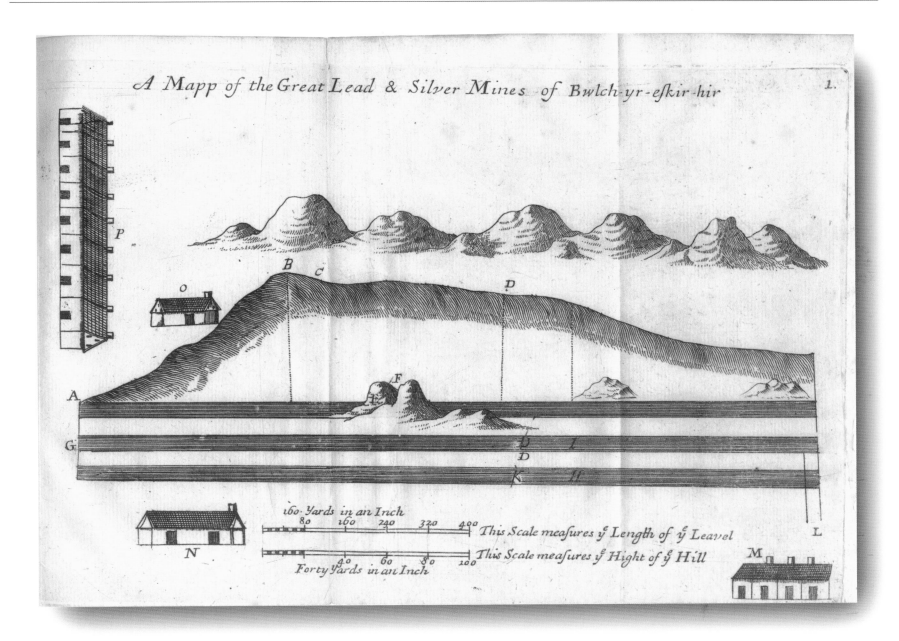

*A Mapp of the Great Lead & Silver Mines of Bwlch-yr-eſkir-hir* 1.

160 Yards in an Inch

80 160 240 320 400

*This Scale meaſures y͏ᵉ Length of y͏ᵉ Leavel*

*This Scale meaſures y͏ᵉ Hight of y͏ᵉ Hill*

40 60 80 100

*Forty Yards in an Inch*

## CANINOG (HAVAN)

This may have been a Myddelton mine and it re-opened many times. The map shows adit B, 88 yards below the summit and, since the incline rises some 500 feet, it must have been about half way up. In September 1705, '*two eminent miners out of Derbyshire*' inspected all the Adventurer's mines and at '*Bwlchir Caninog*' they *went down a shaft ... and find the Veins seven Foot wide, and most of it clean Ore ...*'. However, it had closed before August 1708.

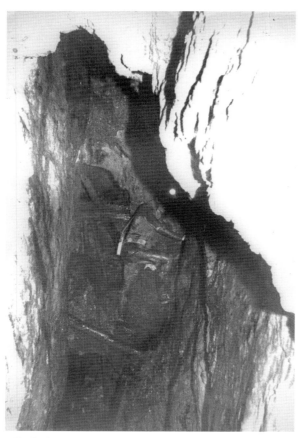

Exploring old stopes at No 4 level, about half-way up the incline, showing timbers and a ladder still in place. The small white circle is the light from Steven Simmons' cap-lamp. 1980.
*Simon Hughes*

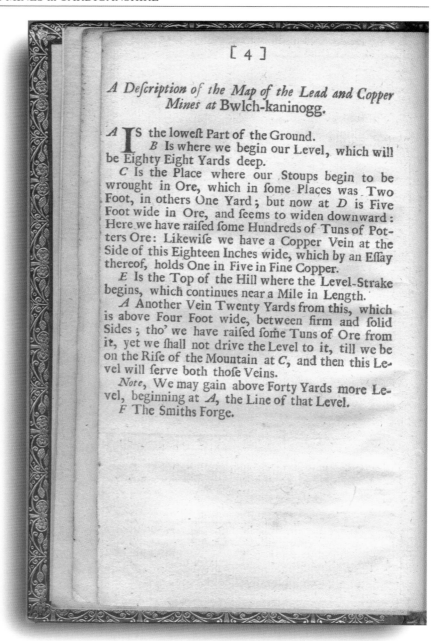

[ 4 ]

*A Description of the Map of the Lead and Copper Mines at* Bwlch-kaninogg.

*A* IS the lowest Part of the Ground.

    *B* Is where we begin our Level, which will be Eighty Eight Yards deep.

    *C* Is the Place where our Stoups begin to be wrought in Ore, which in some Places was Two Foot, in others One Yard; but now at *D* is Five Foot wide in Ore, and seems to widen downward: Here we have raised some Hundreds of Tuns of Potters Ore: Likewise we have a Copper Vein at the Side of this Eighteen Inches wide, which by an Essay thereof, holds One in Five in Fine Copper.

    *E* Is the Top of the Hill where the Level-Strake begins, which continues near a Mile in Length.

    *A* Another Vein Twenty Yards from this, which is above Four Foot wide, between firm and solid Sides; tho' we have raised some Tuns of Ore from it, yet we shall not drive the Level to it, till we be on the Rise of the Mountain at *C*, and then this Level will serve both those Veins.

    *Note*, We may gain above Forty Yards more Level, beginning at *A*, the Line of that Level.

    *F* The Smiths Forge.

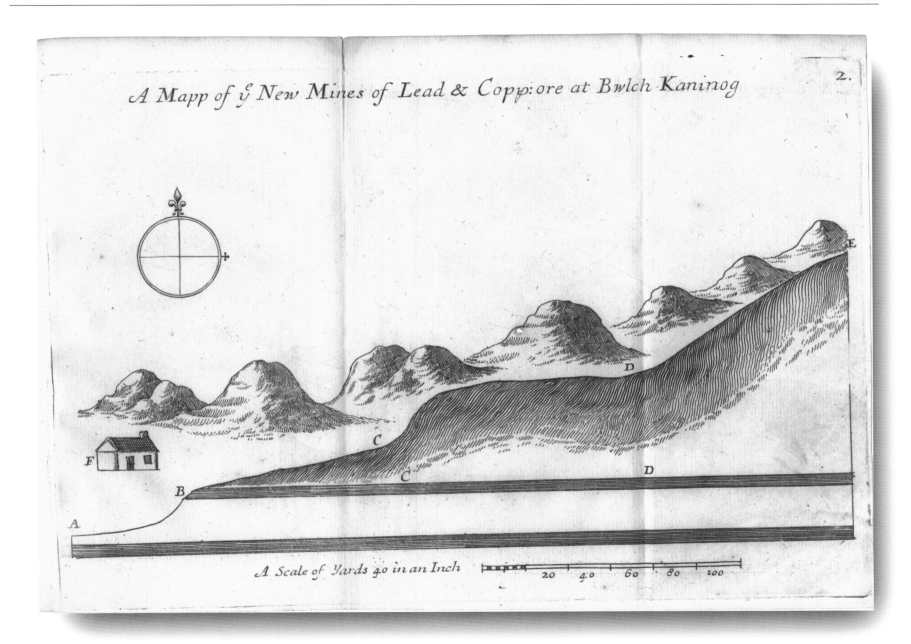

A Mapp of ẙ New Mines of Lead & Copp: ore at Bwlch Kaninog

2.

A Scale of Yards 40 in an Inch        20   40   60   80   100

## CWMSYMLOG

Lewis Morris recorded that Waller had driven Bushell's deep level into fresh ground, '*but he never meddled with the west end nor the bottoms of the great work, the water being too busy and he not skill'd in engines.*'[32,36]

This information is useful, because it suggests that the level on vein G, 116 yards deep, is Bushell's. Allowing for a 20ft rise along its length, this agrees with Ordnance datums for the summit at Pont-ebolion and the adit portal. However, at 64 yards below the crest, Waller's upper level has given rise to a great deal of musing over old plans and in the field. The cross-cut A appears to cut the lode near Blaen y Cwm, now crumbled ruins by the cross-roads. It may have been one of Morris's two levels[37] but now lost. The 64 yards depth might be an error, or was perhaps a level shown on later plans somewhat above Skinner's Shaft.

On 6th September 1705, the Derbyshire miners inspected Cwmsymlog, quoting from the *Description* but, by August 1708, three levels were at work. Bushell's had 17 shafts; the middle level began 200 yards east of it, with ten shafts all on the vein, and the upper one was 28 yards above it with nine shafts, seven being on the vein.[38] How this ties in with the map is left as an exercise for the reader.

Blaen Cwmsymlog, showing ancient workings running uphill from left to right and gradually submerging in forestry. Blaen y Cwm was in the centre of the picture.

*David Bick*

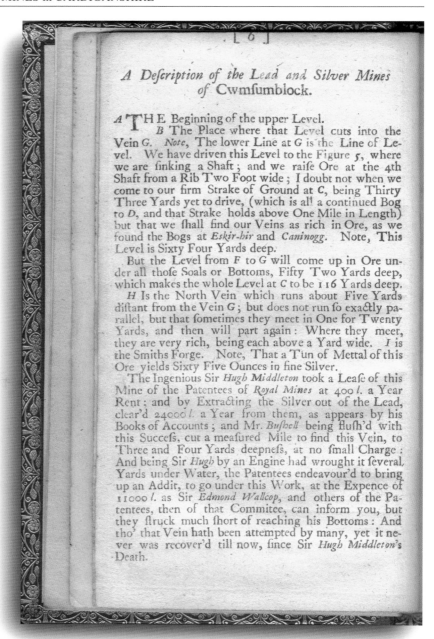

[ 6 ]

*A Description of the Lead and Silver Mines of Cwmsumblock.*

*A* THE Beginning of the upper Level.

*B* The Place where that Level cuts into the Vein G. *Note*, The lower Line at G is the Line of Level. We have driven this Level to the Figure 5, where we are sinking a Shaft; and we raise Ore at the 4th Shaft from a Rib Two Foot wide; I doubt not when we come to our firm Strake of Ground at C, being Thirty Three Yards yet to drive, (which is all a continued Bog to D, and that Strake holds above One Mile in Length) but that we shall find our Veins as rich in Ore, as we found the Bogs at *Eskir-hir* and *Caninogg*. *Note*, This Level is Sixty Four Yards deep.

But the Level from F to G will come up in Ore under all those Soals or Bottoms, Fifty Two Yards deep, which makes the whole Level at C to be 116 Yards deep.

*H* Is the North Vein which runs about Five Yards distant from the Vein G; but does not run so exactly parallel, but that sometimes they meet in One for Twenty Yards, and then will part again: Where they meet, they are very rich, being each above a Yard wide. *I* is the Smiths Forge. *Note*, That a Tun of Mettal of this Ore yields Sixty Five Ounces in fine Silver.

The Ingenious Sir *Hugh Middleton* took a Lease of this Mine of the Patentees of *Royal Mines* at 400 *l*. a Year Rent; and by Extracting the Silver out of the Lead, clear'd 24000 *l*. a Year from them, as appears by his Books of Accounts; and Mr. *Bushell* being flush'd with this Success, cut a measured Mile to find this Vein, to Three and Four Yards deepness, at no small Charge: And being Sir *Hugh* by an Engine had wrought it several Yards under Water, the Patentees endeavour'd to bring up an Addit, to go under this Work, at the Expence of 11000 *l*. as Sir *Edmond Wallcop*, and others of the Patentees, then of that Committee, can inform you, but they struck much short of reaching his Bottoms: And tho' that Vein hath been attempted by many, yet it never was recover'd till now, since Sir *Hugh Middleton's* Death.

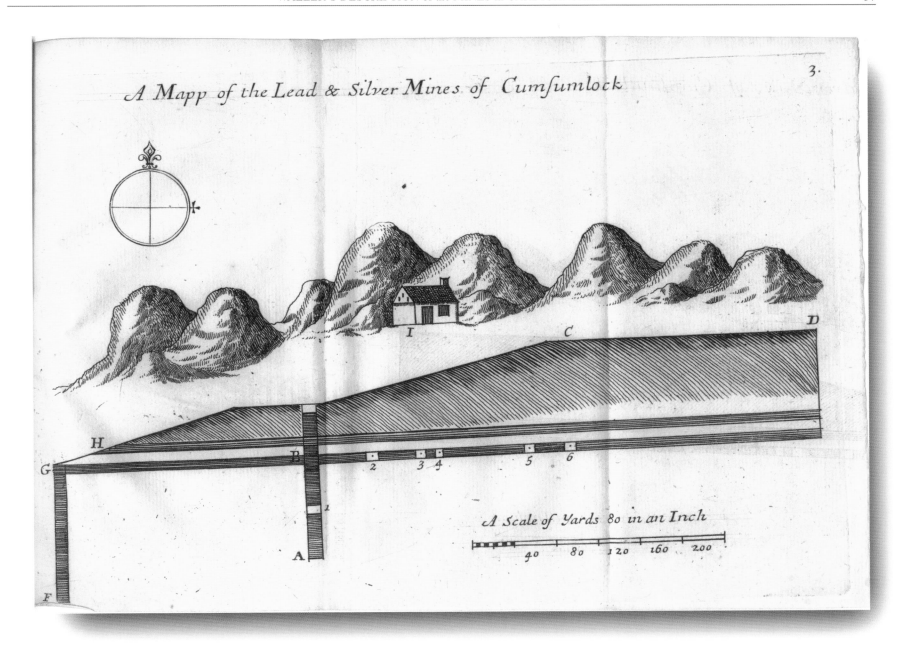

3.

A Mapp of the Lead & Silver Mines of Cumsumlock

A Scale of Yards 80 in an Inch

## GOGINAN

There were three adits, one above the other, and efforts concentrated on draining the old workings. A description of August 1708 reads as follows:

*'Mr Waller has carried on a Level, and driven 300 yards in Length, on which are six Shafts, five of which are on the Vein; the upper Shaft is 36 fathoms deep …'.*

We are then told that Mr Bushell had met a large belly of ore within 30 yards east of this shaft which *'being sunk to the Level, and being sixty Yards under Mr Bushell's Level, Mr Waller expects great Quantities under the Old Belly.'* Bushell's level was presumably driven not far below the surface.

The deep adit emerges by the bridge over the Afon Melindwr and now looks more like a drain. It is a mile long.    *David Bick*

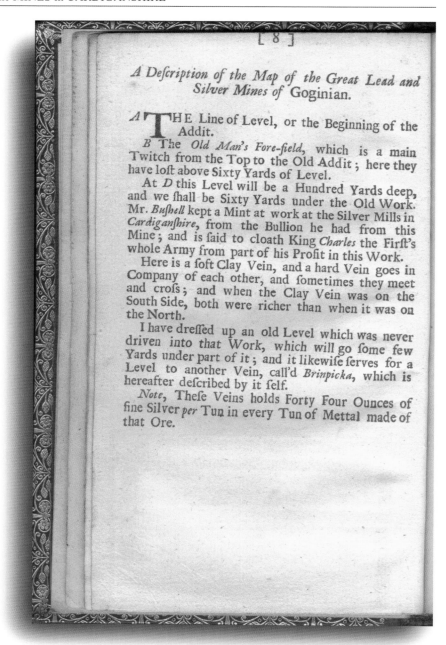

[ 8 ]

*A Description of the Map of the Great Lead and Silver Mines of* Goginian.

A   THE Line of Level, or the Beginning of the Addit.

B  The *Old Man's Fore-field,* which is a main Twitch from the Top to the Old Addit; here they have loft above Sixty Yards of Level.

At *D* this Level will be a Hundred Yards deep, and we fhall be Sixty Yards under the Old Work. Mr. *Bufhell* kept a Mint at work at the Silver Mills in *Cardiganfhire,* from the Bullion he had from this Mine; and is faid to cloath King *Charles* the Firft's whole Army from part of his Profit in this Work.

Here is a foft Clay Vein, and a hard Vein goes in Company of each other, and fometimes they meet and crofs; and when the Clay Vein was on the South Side, both were richer than when it was on the North.

I have dreffed up an old Level which was never driven into that Work, which will go fome few Yards under part of it; and it likewife ferves for a Level to another Vein, call'd *Brinpicka,* which is hereafter defcribed by it felf.

*Note,* Thefe Veins holds Forty Four Ounces of fine Silver *per* Tun in every Tun of Mettal made of that Ore.

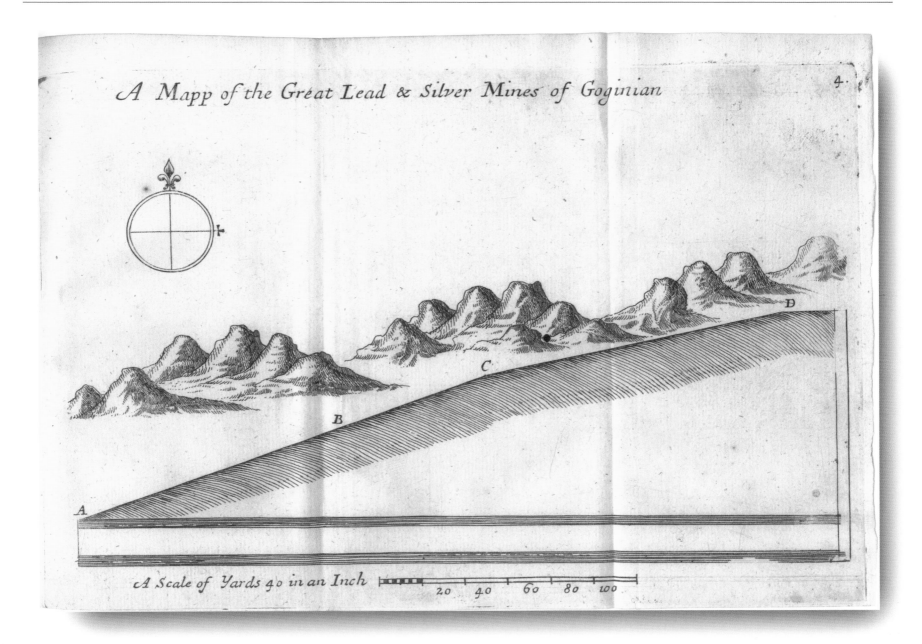

*A Mapp of the Great Lead & Silver Mines of Goginian*

A Scale of Yards 40 in an Inch

## BRYNPICA

From the map, the depth of the level at C scales 46 yards, which agrees well with 18 plus 30 yards from the accompanying text. According to a report made in August 1708, '*the Level is 372 yards in Length, on which is 7 Shafts, of which the uppermost is 17 fathom; they have raised good ore in this vein ...*'.

The level A scales 80 yards long, so that some 290 yards were driven in four years; but the mystery about this site is where it began. Going east from Goginan Fach the lode divided, the workings being apparently on the north branch. Under Goginian, Waller speaks of dressing up an old level which would serve for the Brynpica vein. This must have been deeper than level A and perhaps equates with one on the 25inch Ordnance map in the dingle 200 yards west of Goginan Fach. According to Simon Hughes, it was driven east to the vein but the portal is now lost beneath a car-park.

Just above the road is a run-in cross-cut adit heading for a shaft in the scrub on the outcrop of the lode.                                                                                         *David Bick*

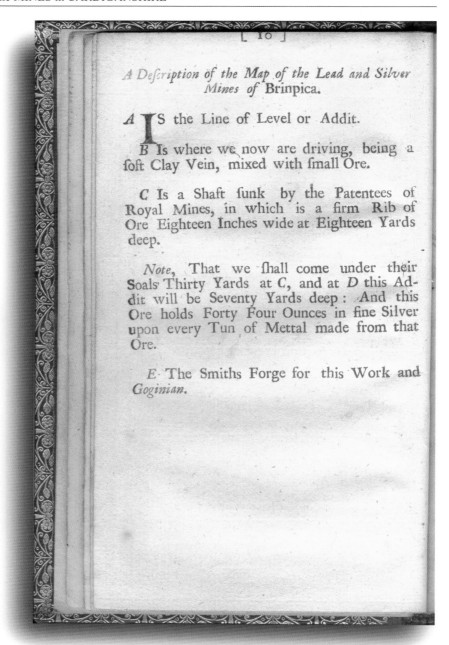

[ 10 ]

*A Description of the Map of the Lead and Silver Mines of* Brinpica.

*A* IS the Line of Level or Addit.

*B* Is where we now are driving, being a foft Clay Vein, mixed with fmall Ore.

*C* Is a Shaft funk by the Patentees of Royal Mines, in which is a firm Rib of Ore Eighteen Inches wide at Eighteen Yards deep.

*Note,* That we fhall come under their Soals Thirty Yards at *C*, and at *D* this Addit will be Seventy Yards deep: And this Ore holds Forty Four Ounces in fine Silver upon every Tun of Mettal made from that Ore.

*E* The Smiths Forge for this Work and *Goginian.*

*A Mapp of the Lead & Silver Mines of Brinpicka.*

*A Scale of Yards 40 in an Inch*

## CWMERVIN (Bwlch)

On the map, BD is on a branch vein and E presumably the Goginan lode, near the ancient trackway (Lewis Morris's *High Road*) between the two. The map seems quite accurate – both as to the length of the cross-cut adit A and the distance to the Goginan lode beyond it.

In September 1705, William Blackwall and Francis Staley, chief Barmaster to the Duke of Rutland, were sent by Mackworth to view the mines and works in Cardiganshire. Their report on '*Blwchir Comervin*' was as follows:

'*The Miners were not at Work, but we were informed that the Level is carried up to the Forefield, and that it wants 45 Yards to the Goginian Vein; that Level is 54 Yards deep, the Ore yields about 44 Ounces of fine Silver in a Ton of Lead.*'

Nearly three years later, another report appeared, this time by order of the General Court:

'*Comarvin runs from West to East, to which they are driving a Level, which is 368 Yards in Length, on which there are 5 Shafts, the uppermost being 40 Yards deep; the Level wants one Fathom to the Vein, which extends to Pencraigthee, being in Length about 1200 Yards.*'

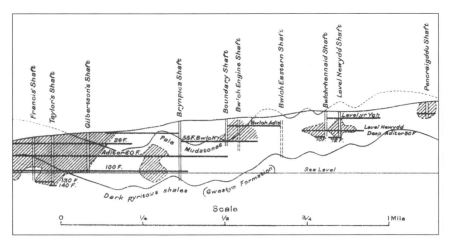

A section along the workings on the Goginan lode at their final extent. Note Waller's Level yr Ych heading towards Pencraigddu.          *O.T. Jones*, 1922

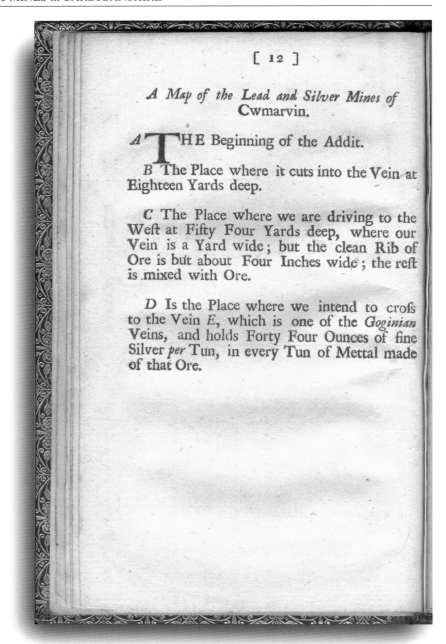

*A Map of the Lead and Silver Mines of* Cwmarvin.

*A* THE Beginning of the Addit.

*B* The Place where it cuts into the Vein at Eighteen Yards deep.

*C* The Place where we are driving to the West at Fifty Four Yards deep, where our Vein is a Yard wide; but the clean Rib of Ore is but about Four Inches wide; the rest is mixed with Ore.

*D* Is the Place where we intend to cross to the Vein *E*, which is one of the *Goginian* Veins, and holds Forty Four Ounces of fine Silver *per* Tun, in every Tun of Mettal made of that Ore.

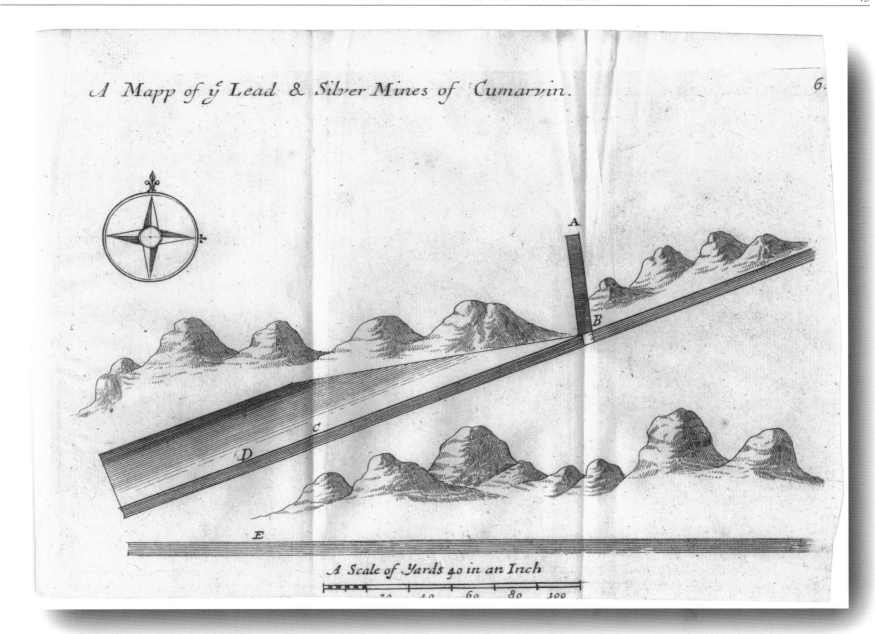

A Mapp of yͤ Lead & Silver Mines of Cumarvin.

6.

A Scale of Yards 40 in an Inch

## PENCRAIGDDU

The map is a puzzle but makes more sense if D were called the South vein, rather than the North. The small level 14 yards deep, long since fallen in, is easily located below the fenced shafts at the mine. The scaled depth at C (64 yards) agrees pretty well with Ordnance datums.

In August 1708, '*the Level is 300 yards, on which is 11 shafts, the uppermost is 22 Fathom deep; and between this Shaft and the Forefield of the Level, is 20 Fathom … Twenty Fathom east from this, is a Shaft formerly sunk, in which they found good ore, but were watered out.*'

Level yr Ych, showing the original high and narrow drivage, and a later widening.                    *Simon Hughes*

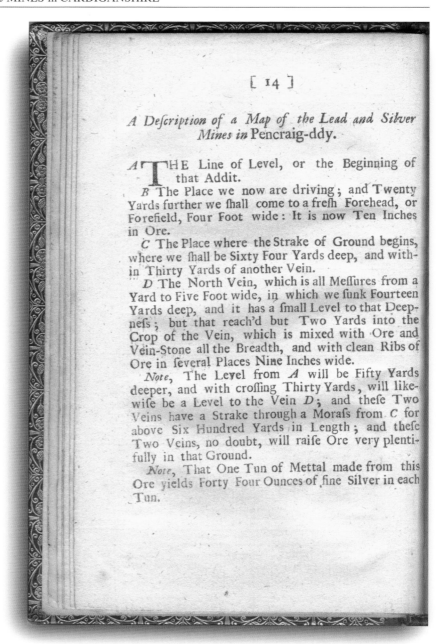

[ 14 ]

*A Description of a Map of the Lead and Silver Mines in* Pencraig-ddy.

*A* THE Line of Level, or the Beginning of that Addit.

*B* The Place we now are driving; and Twenty Yards further we shall come to a fresh Forehead, or Forefield, Four Foot wide: It is now Ten Inches in Ore.

*C* The Place where the Strake of Ground begins, where we shall be Sixty Four Yards deep, and within Thirty Yards of another Vein.

*D* The North Vein, which is all Measures from a Yard to Five Foot wide, in which we sunk Fourteen Yards deep, and it has a small Level to that Deepness; but that reach'd but Two Yards into the Crop of the Vein, which is mixed with Ore and Vein-Stone all the Breadth, and with clean Ribs of Ore in several Places Nine Inches wide.

*Note*, The Level from *A* will be Fifty Yards deeper, and with crossing Thirty Yards, will likewise be a Level to the Vein *D*; and these Two Veins have a Strake through a Morass from *C* for above Six Hundred Yards in Length; and these Two Veins, no doubt, will raise Ore very plentifully in that Ground.

*Note*, That One Tun of Mettal made from this Ore yields Forty Four Ounces of fine Silver in each Tun.

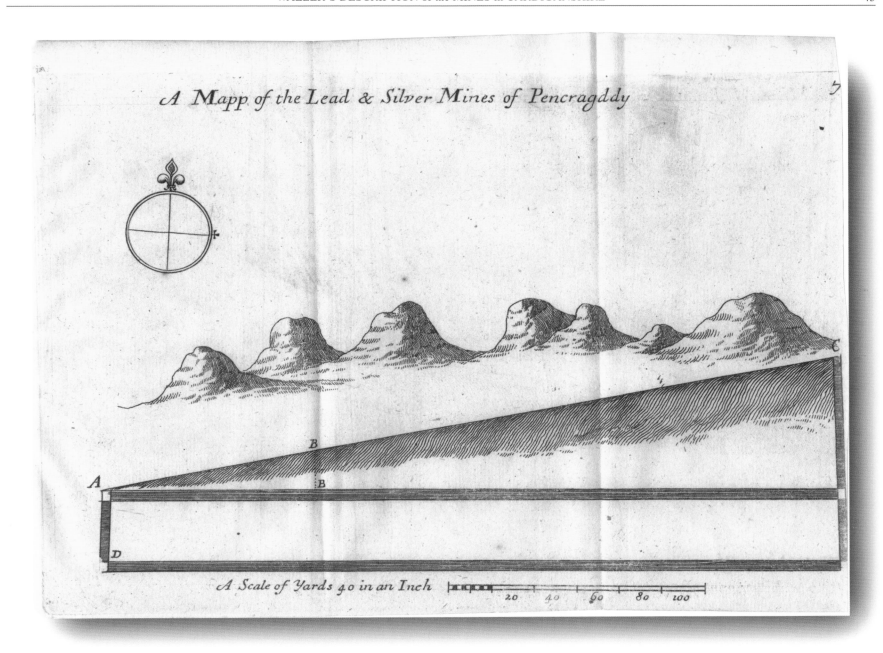

*A Mapp of the Lead & Silver Mines of Pencragddy*

*A Scale of Yards 40 in an Inch*

20    40    60    80    100

## YSTUMTUEN

The adit scales about 50 yards long, entering the lode at B about 17 yards deep, which is about correct and there is good general agreement with Lewis Morris's plan.[40] The reference to bog and watery grounds reflected the common belief that these foretold mineral riches below.

In August 1708, the level was described as 234 yards, '*on which is twelve Shafts: They draw Ore at four Shafts: These Veins being estimated at no more than half a Yard wide, and 30 Yards deep in Ore, which is 1600 in Length, yields in Ore 130200 ton …*'. (This assumes an orebody nearly a mile long in solid galena!)

Looking west along the outcrop in 1989, the scene of much activity three hundred years ago. The adit, only a few fathoms deep, began a little left of the telegraph pole, meeting the lode at the shaft B (white spot) and its trench can be seen just under the wire.
*Brian Jones*

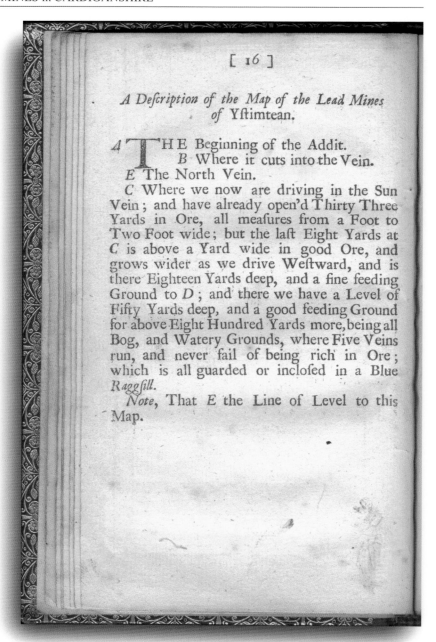

[ 16 ]

*A Description of the Map of the Lead Mines of* Yſtimtean.

*A* THE Beginning of the Addit.
  *B* Where it cuts into the Vein.
*E* The North Vein.
*C* Where we now are driving in the Sun Vein; and have already open'd Thirty Three Yards in Ore, all meaſures from a Foot to Two Foot wide; but the laſt Eight Yards at *C* is above a Yard wide in good Ore, and grows wider as we drive Weſtward, and is there Eighteen Yards deep, and a fine feeding Ground to *D*; and there we have a Level of Fifty Yards deep, and a good feeding Ground for above Eight Hundred Yards more, being all Bog, and Watery Grounds, where Five Veins run, and never fail of being rich in Ore; which is all guarded or incloſed in a Blue *Raggſill*.

  *Note*, That *E* the Line of Level to this Map.

*A Mapp of y*ᵉ *Lead Mines of Yftimtean.*

8

*A Scale of Yards 40 in an Inch*

20    40    60    80    100

## CWMYSTWYTH

This map is unlike the others in showing a level merely as a line but including the stopes, which appear to be in flats rather than the usual vertical deposits. The adit was probably not far above the ruinous stamp mill in Nant-yr-onnen. There was an old stamping house at Cwmsymlog in 1670, so possibly the mill G pre-dated Waller. As for the miners' town and other buildings, we can only guess at their sites.

In August 1708, more tantalising details were given of 'Comystwith old Work': '*It is 13 Foot 8 Inches wide in Ore, mixed with some Vein Stone, excepting that a Rider about 2 Foot interposes towards the Sun-side. Sixteen Yards above this, in the same Vein, they are working in Ore … Sun [south] of this lies a Belly Vein, which is driven 132 Yards, and is a common level to all the Works. Twenty Yards above this Level, is a Drift carryed on 47 Yards … On this Belly Vein are four Shafts; the upper Shaft is 68 Yards deep …*'.

If one of these levels was A on the map, it is hard to explain how '*Cumistwith Vein near the Stamping Mill, is near the top of the Mountain, has a Level of 66 Yards, on which are two Shafts; the upper is 22 Yards deep … Mr Waller found that the old Man had a rich Belly of 5 Yards in Ore, but was watered* out …'. How did this relate to the old Work? Perhaps some of these mysteries will one day be resolved.

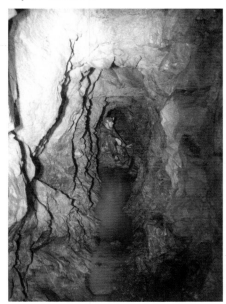

Ivor Richards takes a rest just inside the collapsed entrance to Nantrefach Adit. In the foreground, a groove worn by wheelbarrows can be seen. *Robert Protheroe Jones, 1988*

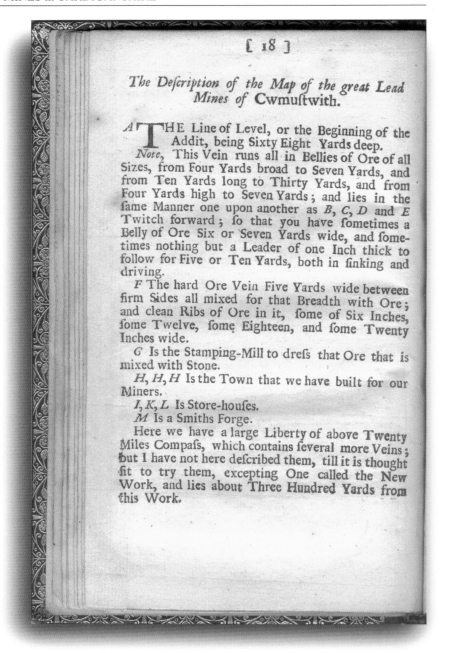

[ 18 ]

*The Description of the Map of the great Lead Mines of* Cwmuſtwith.

A THE Line of Level, or the Beginning of the Addit, being Sixty Eight Yards deep.

*Note,* This Vein runs all in Bellies of Ore of all Sizes, from Four Yards broad to Seven Yards, and from Ten Yards long to Thirty Yards, and from Four Yards high to Seven Yards; and lies in the ſame Manner one upon another as *B, C, D* and *E* Twitch forward; ſo that you have ſometimes a Belly of Ore Six or Seven Yards wide, and ſometimes nothing but a Leader of one Inch thick to follow for Five or Ten Yards, both in ſinking and driving.

*F* The hard Ore Vein Five Yards wide between firm Sides all mixed for that Breadth with Ore; and clean Ribs of Ore in it, ſome of Six Inches, ſome Twelve, ſome Eighteen, and ſome Twenty Inches wide.

*G* Is the Stamping-Mill to dreſs that Ore that is mixed with Stone.

*H, H, H* Is the Town that we have built for our Miners.

*I, K, L* Is Store-houſes.

*M* Is a Smiths Forge.

Here we have a large Liberty of above Twenty Miles Compaſs, which contains ſeveral more Veins; but I have not here deſcribed them, till it is thought fit to try them, excepting One called the New Work, and lies about Three Hundred Yards from this Work.

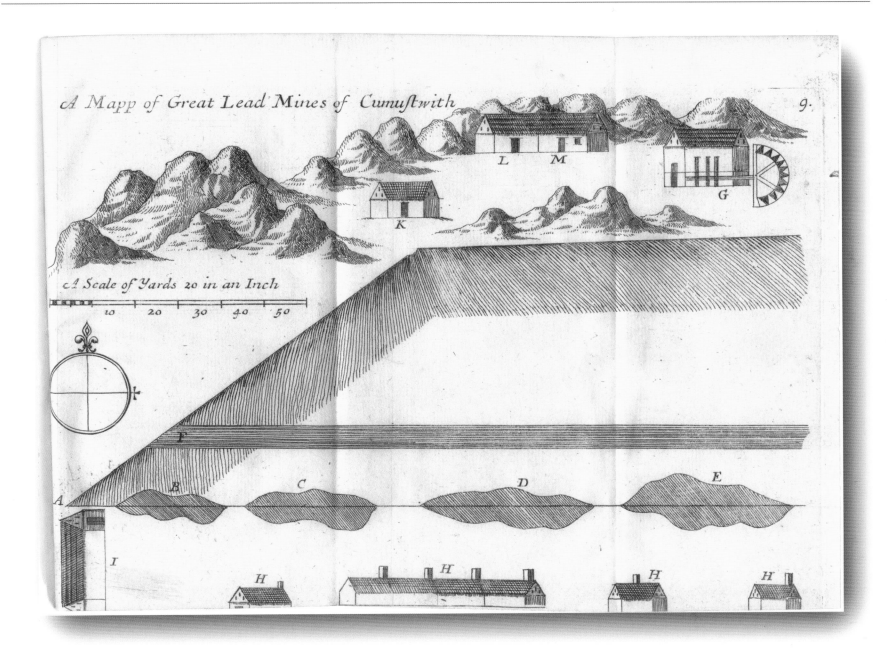

A Mapp of Great Lead Mines of Cumustwith

A Scale of Yards 20 in an Inch

## CWMYSTWYTH NEW MINES

Waller informs us that this was about 300 yards away (from the stamp-mill area?) but trials were being made far and wide, so the identity is uncertain but it is quite probably the Nantrefach Level.[41]

According to a report of August 1708, '*Cumystwith Nanstrevach runs from S.E. to N. W. and holds good Potters Ore. There is a level 103 Yards, on which is one shaft 59 Yards deep: The Forefield where they are now working is 2 Foot wide, of which there is 9 Inches of Potters Ore, which mends daily … the Ground unwrought is about a measured Mile … This mine, at 9 Inches wide, 20 Yards deep, and 1000 Yards long, will yield in Ore 27125 Ton; the Value whereof at £1 per Ton clear of all Charges, is £27125.*'

The forecast, like all the others, was to prove somewhat optimistic.

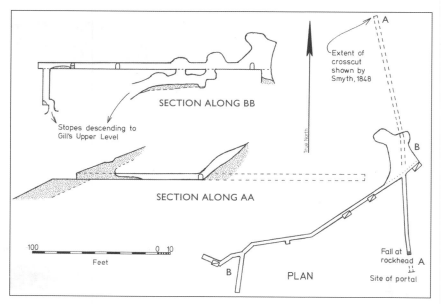

A recent plan and section of Waller's Nantrefach workings, which may have been subsequently extended.

*Robert Protheroe Jones*

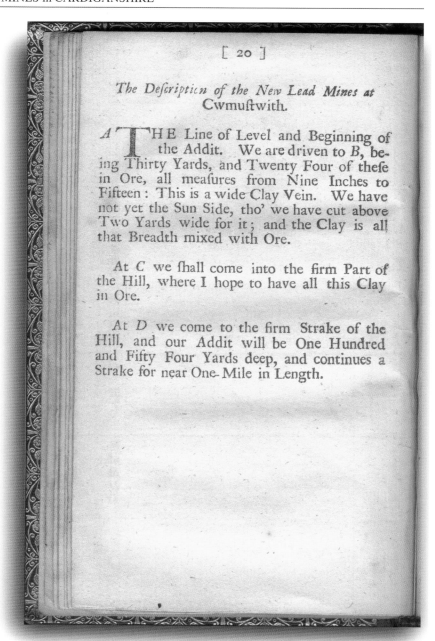

[ 20 ]

*The Description of the New Lead Mines at Cwmustwith.*

*A* THE Line of Level and Beginning of the Addit. We are driven to *B*, being Thirty Yards, and Twenty Four of these in Ore, all measures from Nine Inches to Fifteen: This is a wide Clay Vein. We have not yet the Sun Side, tho' we have cut above Two Yards wide for it; and the Clay is all that Breadth mixed with Ore.

At *C* we shall come into the firm Part of the Hill, where I hope to have all this Clay in Ore.

At *D* we come to the firm Strake of the Hill, and our Addit will be One Hundred and Fifty Four Yards deep, and continues a Strake for near One-Mile in Length.

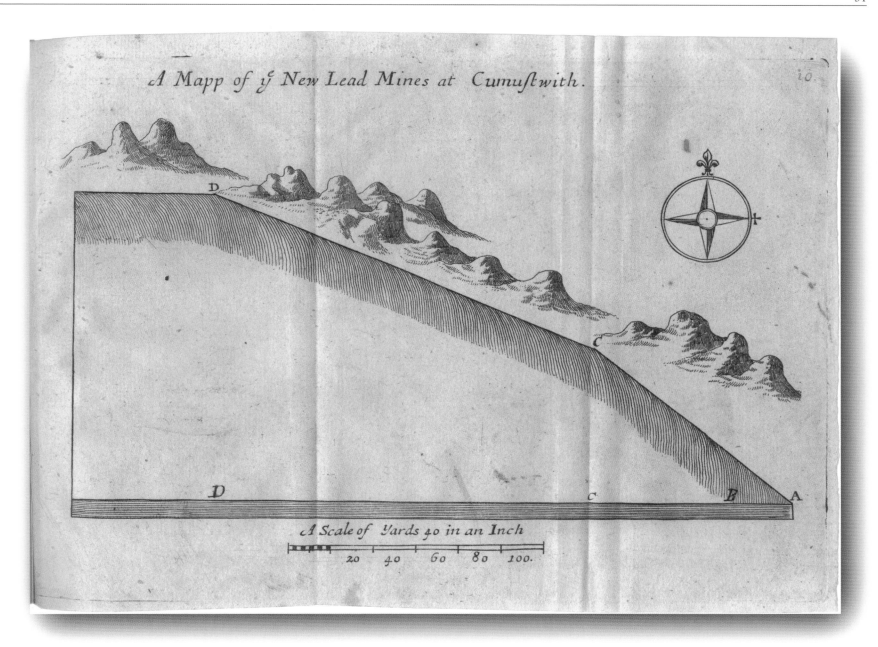

*A Mapp of y<sup>e</sup> New Lead Mines at Cumuſtwith.*

A Scale of Yards 40 in an Inch

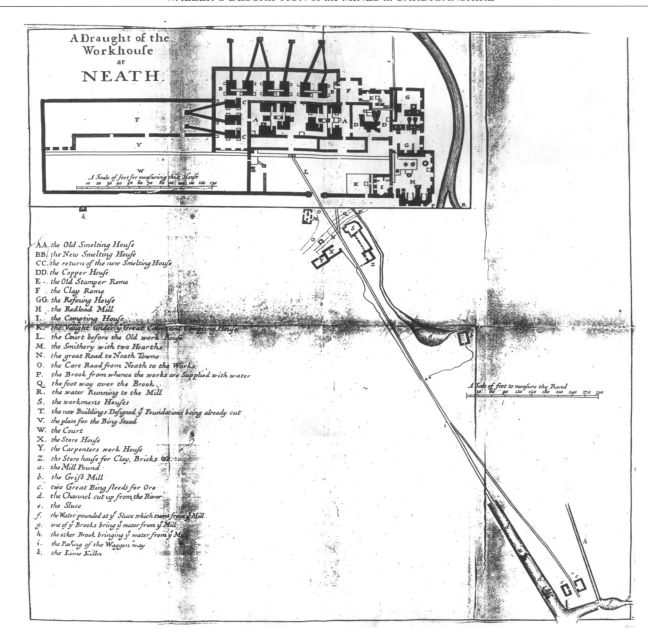

A Draught of the
Workhouse
at
NEATH.

A Scale of feet for measuring this House
10  20  30  40  50  60  70  80  90  100  110  120  130

AA. the Old Smelting House
BB. the New Smelting House
CC. the return of the new Smelting House
DD. the Copper House
E . the Old Stamper Rome
F . the Clay Rome
GG. the Refining House
H . the Redlead Mill
I . the Compting House
K. the Vaught under ye Great Cellar and Compting House
L . the Court before the Old work house
M. the Smithery with two Hearths
N . the great Road to Neath Towne
O. the Cart Road from Neath to the Works
P. the Brook from whence the works are Supplied with water
Q. the foot way over the Brook
R. the water Running to the Mill
S. the workmens Houses
T. the new Buildings Designed ye Foundations being already cut
V. the place for the Bing Stead
W. the Court
X. the Store House
Y. the Carpenters work House
Z. the Store house for Clay, Bricks &c.
a. the Mill Pound
b. the Grist Mill
c. two Great Bing steeds for Ore
d. the Channel cut up from the River
e. the Sluce
f. the Water pounded at ye Sluce which runs from ye Mill
g. one of ye Brooks bring ye water from ye Mill
h. the other Brook bringing ye water from ye Mill
i. the Paring of the Waggon way
k. the Lime Killn

A Scale of feet to measure the Road
30  60  90  120  150  180  210  240  270  300

## THE WORKHOUSE AT NEATH (opposite)

The works pre-dated Swansea as the centre for smelting by over 20 years. The plan comprises two drawings in one – the whole area and a larger scale insert. Mackworth's original smeltery is defined by AA, DD, E and F. The Refining House, GG, was the first addition during Robert Lydall's period at the site, closely followed by the Redlead Mill, H, the Compting House (office), I, and the vault or store-room, K. All this was completed in 1699.

In the frenzied expansion of 1703-4, some at least of the old furnaces were reconstructed, also the New Smelting House, BB, CC, with its nine furnaces (which may not all have been built). Then seems to have followed T, V and W, new buildings and court presumably intended for more furnaces but halted by the sudden economies.

From the three furnaces in CC, the new building T includes their flues and chimneys, which before were outside. Within the Old and New Smelting Houses are 17 large reverberatory furnaces, each one scaling about 14 feet by 9 feet. In the New Smelting House, the long horizontal flues lead to six chimney stacks. The other eight furnaces appear to have had high chimneys in the centre of AA. Two more furnaces for copper are shown in DD, the Copper House. One is described as for refining, the other was a blast furnace known to have been used for melting iron amongst other things and fuelled by 'Pitt Coale Charr'd', i.e. coke. Two large bellows are connected to it.

The Refining House, GG, had six furnaces with room for two more, arranged in three pairs. The house was built to include the 26ft waterwheel with its launder and this is shown as a long rectangle, with shaft leading to the stamping mill in E and to the bellows in DD. The wheel also powered the small bellows for the refining furnaces. F was the Clay Rome (room), with a room above for turning Stourbridge clay into heat-resistant bricks. In the Redlead Mill, litharge was heated, if necessary, and then ground by pairs of millstones into red lead, a 20 foot waterwheel being provided at the left side for the purpose. The Redlead Mill is said to have been on a lower level than the Refining House, so that the two waterwheels operated in series.

Litharge and red lead were in demand for glassmaking and for pottery glazes. By the winter of 1708, work must have been pretty slack, for the plumber was ordered 'to proceed in making Flower potts, and that T. Hawkins send up by way of Glo'ster all such fflower potts as are ready made.'[42]

Outside the mill itself are some associated buildings, part of the canal that Mackworth had built from the Neath River and the waggon-way from the dock. This very early railway, with horse-drawn waggons running on oak rails on oak sleepers, reflects Mackworth's innovative nature; the idea is said to have come from Shropshire. He had installed one of these to the north of the Melincrythan mills, to transport the coal from his mines down to the River Neath. To save on the horses needed, the waggons were fitted with a sail. Waller saw these and commented 'for the cheap Carriage of his Coal to the Water-side, Whereby one horse does the Work of ten at all times; but when any wind is stirring (which is seldom wanting near the Sea) one Man and a small Sail does the work of twenty.' The situation at the mill was different in that they needed to transport heavy loads of ore up the hillside. In one letter from Lydall, a sailing waggon is being made but in the meantime they are experimenting with another waggon to take loads across the marshy ground. This is to run on rollers made from 'Great Gunns', apparently scrap iron cannons. He writes, 'four horses doe with the greatest ease imaginable draw them, or rather role them over the soft Marsh and up the hill to the Works altho they weigh at least a tun and halfe.'

The subsequent history of the Neath works is one of decline and a detailed survey of all the mills in August 1708 put the total furnaces at seventeen. Of these, there were probably two for smelting, both at Garreg and the Silver Mills, plus two refining furnaces at Garreg. In surveying the effort that went into these four works, especially at Neath, there is something deeply tragic that in the end it all came to nothing, or at least, nearly so. In fact, after the bitter controversies of 1709-10, Mackworth, never one to admit defeat, eventually revived copper smelting in his home town and the works were not finally demolished until about the early 1800s. Today, only the line of the waggon-way survives as a road leading down towards the river from Neath, where with such high aspirations it all began over three centuries ago.[43]

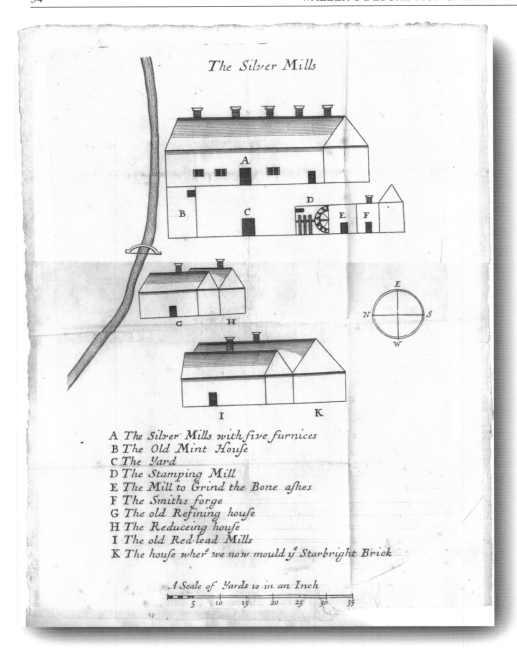

A *The Silver Mills with five furnices*
B *The Old Mint House*
C *The Yard*
D *The Stamping Mill*
E *The Mill to Grind the Bone ashes*
F *The Smiths forge*
G *The old Refining house*
H *The Reduceing house*
I *The old Red-lead Mills*
K *The house wher² we now mould y² Starbright Brick*

*A Scale of Yards 10 in an Inch*
     5    10    15    20    25    30    35

## THE SILVER MILLS, Grid ref. SN 685950

This historic site probably dates back to the 1620s and perhaps before. In 1755 it was demolished for a charcoal blast-furnace for iron-ore, which still survives as Dyfi Furnace, now a Scheduled Monument and open to the public.

It appears the works were on either side of the A487(T) road, as denoted by the little bridge. A is the smelting house used by the company and probably rebuilt since the old silver mills. In the 1640s, silver coins were minted in the Old Mint House B, where in 1667 Pettus (opposite page) tells us was a '*great Iron-bound Chest with three Locks, … with old defaced Stamps therein.*'

Slags and bone-ashes were originally processed at D and E by wet and dry stampers. E is now shown as having stones or edge-runners to grind the ashes, and the records show that six stampers went to a stamp mill at Cwmystwyth in 1701. The plan shows only three head of stamps at D but how much reliance can be placed on this is uncertain. The building itself is mentioned in a deed of 1776 and some foundation stones still visible may testify to its actual site. Under K, '*Starbright*' is probably a corruption of Stourbridge.

## THE LEAD MILLS, Grid ref. SN 653890

Waller's key map, item 13, mentions four hearths and bellows, driven by one wheel but no plan has come to light. The site, now private property, was later adapted for other purposes. There are various buildings and leats cut in the solid rock, some of which may well date from the 17th century.

**Opposite page:** This inventory from *Fodinae Regales* describes the Silver Mills in 1667. Pettus was unreliable and even the number of men employed is inconsistent. He states it was ten but the numbers quoted add up to twelve.

*Fodinæ Regales.*

## Chap. XXV.
### Of the Silver Mills.

About three miles from *Tallibont* there is a certain Stream of Water, which falls into four great *Wheels*, whose Turning guides the rising and falling of the *Bellows*, and *Stampers* which belong to the *Hearths* and *Furnaces*, for *Smelting*, *Stamping* and *Refining*. And that the Nature of them may the better be known, here followeth a Particular taken in *Anno* 1667, of all *Utensils* and *Attendances* to them belonging.

### At the great Smelting Mills.

Five Hearths with Backs, Cheeks, Workstones, Iron Plates, and other necessaries.

Five Pair of large Smelting Bellows with Beams, Frames, Swords, Triddles, Cogs, and all things to them appertaining; one new large Water-wheel with Water-troughs, Sluices, and other necessaries convenient for working the said five Hearths.

One great Pair of Scales, with ten Half-hundred Weights of Lead, and other small Weights needful.

Three Wooden Measures for White Cole, six Wheel-barrows, six Shovels of Iron, with Iron Forks and Tongs, five Moulds, and a Ladle for Casting.

And to these belong 10 Men, and these five Hearths may well imploy 500 Miners.

### In the Oar-house.

One great Beam with Scales and Iron Chains, and several Weights for Oar.

1 Man.

### In the Old Mint-house.

One Pair of small Bellows, one Wind-Furnace to melt Silver in, made with Brick and Iron bars; one large Beam of Iron, and Brass Scales, with several piles of Brass Weights, and other Weights to weigh Silver with; one great Iron-bound Chest with three Locks, formerly used for the Coyners there, with old defaced Stamps therein, one Table-counter with Cupboards, Shelves, &c.

1 Man.

### In the Stamping Mills.

One large Shed lately erected over certain Stampers, with a new Frame for them; three sets of Stampers, one for wet Slags, one for dry, and one for Bone-ashes, all faced with Iron, and beat upon great Iron Planks cast for the purpose only; one large Water-wheel with Troughs, &c. for drawing the said Stamps, and the annexed Mill to grind Bone-ashes, with a pair of Stones, and all things necessary for Grinding and Sifting bone-ashes in order to Refining.

1 Man.

One Smiths shop with Bellows, Tongs, Anvils, Hammers, Vice, Sledges, Grindstone, &c. thereunto appertaining.

1 Man.

Six great Tubs (of Cask) Buddles, Sieves, Rakes, Shovels, and other necessaries for washing and cleansing of Slags.

2 Men.

### At the Refining Mill.

Several Troughs and Sluces for the conveying of Water to the Mill, one large new Wheel, that carrieth

three Pair of bellows, with Swords, Beams, Truddles, Frames, Cogs, and all things appertaining in good order.

One Pair of very large bellows for the Test onely, with a great Frame or Model of Iron cast, to make the Test in, with a great Cap of Stone in a Case of Iron fit for Refining; as also an Ergine or Winlace, with Ropes and Pullies to draw up the same, with several Refining Irons, Feeding Plate of Iron, Tongs, Furnace with Iron door, grates, and bars of Iron, &c. necessary thereto, one pair of reducing bellows and furnace to melt the Litharidge into Lead, after refining with Irons, &c. necessary thereunto.

2 Men.

One Pair of bellows and Furnace for melting of Slags, with Iron bars, Shovels, &c. necessary thereunto; one planck'd Plate for tempering the bone-ashes with beaters, and a Room made fit to lay Corn in.

2 Men.

### At the Red Lead Mill.

One great Water-wheel, with several Sluces, Troughs and Dams thereunto belonging; four Pair of stones for grinding Red Lead, one large Oven with several Chimnies for making and colouring Red Lead, with Iron forks, Rakes, Shovels, &c. for the same; as also one great Iron Door and Door case to the said Oven, and two other Iron Doors in Iron Frames, with Iron gates and bars to the Fire-hearths of the said Oven. One great Copper Bason to wash Red Lead in, one Iron Ladle, Tunnel, &c. one great Beam and Scales to weigh Red Lead with, several sets of Coopers Tools, great Plains, &c. necessary for making Red Lead Cask.

2 Men.

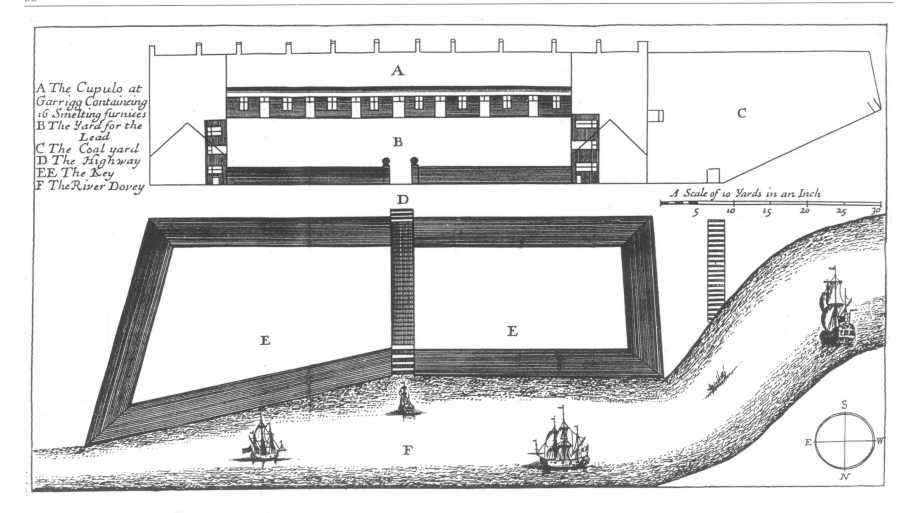

A The Cupulo at
Garrigg Containing
16 Smelting furnices
B The Yard for the
Lead
C The Coal yard
D The Highway
EE The Key
F The River Dovey

A Scale of 10 Yards in an Inch

## The Cupola at Garrigg, Grid ref. SN 694968

A cupola was built somewhere at Garreg in 1700 but, from the beginning, it seems that the Mine Adventurer's works were never pursued with vigour, nor even fully completed. The combined plan and elevation (reduced in size) has been inverted, the River Dovey being to the north-west and not to the south-east. Building did not begin until 1703, the cupola and quay being separated by the road, now the A487(T), and the properties called Park Terrace no doubt occupy the site of the former. The chimneys rose up from behind the long building and not from the ridge, as appears in the drawing. The 16 furnaces were probably never installed, being a victim of cut-backs in 1704.

It appears that the building of Glandyfi station and its yard later destroyed all evidence of the Key.

Glandyfi station and the River Dovey on an old picture postcard, c.1930. It was built in the early 1860s (opening on 1st July 1863) near the site of Garrigg Key. The cupola was out of the picture to the right of the car and the Key was under the railway line, near the signal, with the refining houses and refining houses just beyond and to the right of the station.                    *Neil Parkhouse collection*

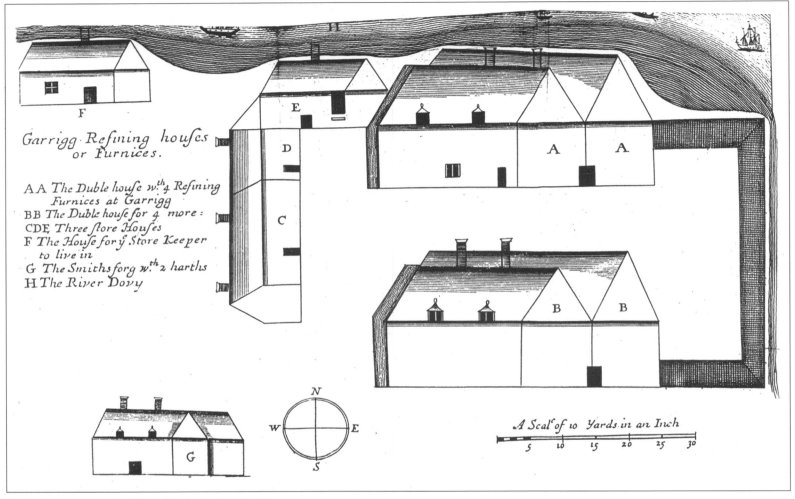

Garrigg Refining houses or Furnices.

AA The Duble house w.th 4 Refining Furnices at Garrigg
BB The Duble house for 4 more:
CDE Three store Houses
F The House for y Store Keeper to live in
G The Smiths forg w.th 2 harths
H The River Dovy

A Scale of 10 Yards in an Inch

## GARRIGG REFINING HOUSES, Grid ref. SN 696970

These probably stood on made-up ground east of Station House. Slag has been found on site but it may have come from elsewhere. The total size implies more than eight furnaces but there is no evidence that even those had been built at the time. The ends of buildings A and B show wavy lines suggesting launders for water-wheels to blow the furnaces and a reservoir dating from before 1787 on the nearby Afon Melindwr was perhaps intended for the purpose.

In contrast to the well-established Silver Mills, it seems that neither of the Garreg sites included a stamping mill.

Activity revived to an extent in 1707 and after 1710 Garreg was used for some years both for smelting and administration. Henry Bowdler of Shrewsbury revived the works around 1760-70 but they eventually declined into storehouses and were finally demolished.

# REFERENCES

1 Rees, William, *Industry before the Industrial Revolution*, Vol II, 1968. This is the most detailed general account but see also Scott, W.R., *Constitution and Finance of English, Scottish and Irish Joint Stock Companies to 1720*, Vol II, 1912 (Reprinted 1951); Lewis, Samuel, *The Activities of the Governor and Company of the Mine Adventurers of England*, 1950 (Thesis, National Library of Wales); Lewis, W.J., *Lead Mining in Wales*, 1967. To Robert Hunt must go the credit for the first account, in *Memoirs of the Geological Survey*, 1848, but unfortunately it is full of errors in spite of the author's assertion of every care being taken. For an introduction to the archaeology of Welsh Potosi, see Marilyn Palmer, 'The Richest in all Wales', NMRS, *British Mining 22,* 1983. See also Bick, David, 'Early Mining Leats and Ponds in Wales', PDMHS, *Mining Before Powder*, 1994, 37-40. Why the company styled itself the Mine Adventurers *of England* has never been explained.

2 Bick, David, 'Bronze Age Copper Mining in mid-Wales – Fact or Fantasy?', *JHMS,* 1999, Vol 33 No.1 The only certain verification of copper-smelting is copper-slag or furnaces, which have never yet been found.

3 Boon, George C. 'A Case-History of British Bullion: Cardiganshire Silver and the Feathers Coinage 1671-1731'. *Brit. Numis. Journ.*, 1993, 65-83. The silver could vary in different parts of the lode. In the 19th century, the best mines were Penycefn (Court Grange), 37.8 oz, and South Daren, 36.1. Cwmsymlog rated at only 22.7. Goginan (1837-44) yielded 25.3 oz, later falling to 18.2 oz. (O.T. Jones, *M.G.S. Special Reports Vol XX*, 1922, 194)

4 Boon, George C. *Cardiganshire Silver and the Aberystwyth Mint,* 1981

5 Aubrey, John, *Brief Lives*, ed. Anthony Powell, 1949, 368

6 Waller was with William Powell of Nanteos, a shareholder in Esgairhir, when he met Mackworth. See Waller, *The Mine Adventure Laid Open,* 1710

7 A reprint appeared in 1702; copies are very rare. For Mackworth's involvement, see West Glam. Arch. Service, NAS Gn/1 1/2. It is unlikely that the true story will ever come out.

8 'Minutes of the Select Committee … held at Sir Humphry Mackworth's Chambers in Lincoln's Inn', 8th July 1699. Swansea Museum

9 J.H.C., Vol XVI, 360

10 'Minutes of the Select Committee,' 2nd February 1702

11 Metalliferous mines were not obliged to keep plans until 1872, with small ones exempt even then.

12 Bick, David, *The Old Metal Mines of Mid-Wales Part 6,* 1991, 11-17

13 Rees, William, 556

14 Waller, William, *The Mine Adventure Laid Open,* 1710, 61

15 W.R. Scott, 444 -58

16 Mormon International Genealogical Index.

17 Information from Michael Gill.

18 Lewis, W.J., 79. I have not had time to check his sources. For Waller's introduction to Wales, see *The Mine Adventure Laid Open,* 1710, ii

19 *The Mine Adventure, Proposed by Sir Humphrey Mackworth,* 1698

20 Phillips, D. Rhys, *The History of the Vale of Neath,* 1925, 272. Roger Bird has shown that Anne Waller was Mackworth's maternal grandmother. If a daughter of hers had married William's father, the link would be explained. John Aubrey tells us that Edmund Waller was related to Oliver Cromwell.

21 Llanbadarn Parish Register, NAS Gn/I 1/2

22 Scott, W.R., 457. Mackworth, *Book of Vouchers,* 1711, Second Part, 16

23 For comments on Cadw and the Scheduling process in practice, see Bick, David, 'Bryngwyn Colliery', *Archive* 38, 2003, 41,42

24 Bick, David, *Part 3*, 53-61

25 Bick, David and Davies, Philip Wyn, *Lewis Morris and the Cardiganshire Mines,* 1994, 31

26 'Minutes of the Select Committee', 2nd February 1702

27 A large-scale plan, with signs of up-dating, in Ceridigion Archives shows the West Level driven on a north lode, then switching to a south lode. The basic plan omits the new road from Talybont, so it may well be pre-1840. (A local farmer told me the road was surveyed and pegged out from the top of Moel y Llyn, to the north.)

28 Dickinson, H.W., *Sir Samuel Morland,* 1970

29 John Aubrey relates that although Myddelton took the credit for the New River, the idea was not his own.

30 Wade, Ted., *The Plynlimon & Hafan Tramway,* 2000

31 William Rees, 441,2

32 Bick, David, *Part 6,* 32-37

33 Bick, David, *Part 3,* 6-9

34 Mackworth, *Book of Vouchers,* Second Part, 1711, 19

35 Hughes, Simon J.S., 'The Cwmystwyth Mines', *NMRS, B. M. No.17,* 1983

36 Mackworth, 1711, 21

37 Bick and Davies, 13, 57

38 Mackworth, *Book of Vouchers*, 1711, Second Part, 5, 36

39 The leat began at a dam (710830) high above Ceunant mine, crossing the old High Road to Machynlleth via Esgairhir and serving Pencraigddu on the way. It bears the hallmarks of antiquity.

40 Bick and Davies, 42

41 For possible locations of the various workings, see recent *Welsh Mines Society Newsletters*. The subject arouses continuing discussion. For the archaeology of the area, see Armfield, Colin, 'Dressing Floors on Copa Hill, Cwmystwyth', *AW,* 1989, Vol 29. See also Simon J.S.Hughes, 1983

42 Grant-Francis, G, *Smelting of Copper in the Swansea District,* 1881, 95

43 The plan of the works in 1720, (Rees, 536), has errors.

## GLOSSARY

| | |
|---|---|
| ADIT | A tunnel driven for drainage and access. |
| BELLY | A mass of ore in the lode. |
| BLEND(E) | Zinc sulphide, an ore of zinc, then of low value. |
| BING | A north-country measure. Waller allowed four bings per ton of lead, *Essay*, 1698, 15 |
| BING STEAD | Enclosure for storing ore. |
| BOTTOMS | The deepest part of the workings. |
| COPPER-PYRITES | Copper and iron sulphide, the common ore of copper. |
| CRANCH | A pillar of lode or rock left to support the workings. |
| CROSS-CUT | A level driven through barren strata to the lode. |
| DRESSING | Separating the pure ore from the waste or gangue surrounding it. |
| FATHOM | Six feet, the miner's unit of measurement. |
| FLAT-RODS | Iron rods, each about 20ft, in a long line to transmit power from a waterwheel or engine to a pumping shaft. |
| FOREFIELD | The furthermost part of the workings. |
| FOREHEAD | As forefield. |
| GANGUE | Rock, quartz etc enclosing the valuable mineral. |
| GALENA | Lead sulphide, the common ore, containing up to 86% lead metal. |
| GREEN ORE | Usually malachite, an ore of copper. |
| KIBBLE | A barrel-like container in which ore was raised. |
| LEVEL | A horizontal tunnel driven from the surface or from underground. The term was often interchangeable with Adit. |
| LIBERTY | An area of land leased for mining. |
| OLD MAN | An ancient term for all previous miners. |
| ORE | Ore is the mineral as it comes from the mine. Dressed ore is the concentrated mineral after removing waste rock etc. |
| POTTER'S ORE | Galena containing very little silver. |
| QUARTZ | Silicon dioxide, a worthless and very hard white mineral often found in the lodes. |
| RIDER | A mass of rock dividing a lode. |
| RISE | An underground shaft driven upwards. |
| SHAFT | A well-like excavation from the surface for working the lode. |
| STOPE | Cavities left by the removal of ore. |
| SOUGH | A north-country term for an adit. |
| SUN VEIN | A vein to the south of another working. |
| TWITCH | The closing-in of the walls of a lode. |
| VEIN | Another term for a lode. |
| WHIM | A windlass worked by horses or other means. |

## ACKNOWLEDGMENTS

In compiling this little volume, I have been immeasurably assisted by friends who have generously rendered help and made available material of all kinds. From the many dialogues and almost endless ponderings both in the study and the field, at least a better understanding nearly always ensued. For in our haste for the right answer, we sometimes forget that to ask the right question is the best beginning of all.

In particular I have to thank Simon Hughes, born at the Lead Mills in Talybont, whose knowledge of the records and the physical testimony of the mines above ground and below has been invaluable. Roger Bird has been unstinting in his researches, not least into the development of the Garreg and Neath works. His general comments have kept the narrative 'on the rails' and the text describing the plans of the smelting sites has drawn largely upon his writings. A bibliography of the Mine Adventure has long been wanted and, at short notice, Robert Protheroe Jones of the National Museums & Galleries of Wales has kindly provided a select version, with the promise of further details before long.

Susan Ashmole and my son William have joined me on field-trips, and helped with proof reading and in designing the book. In tracing the origins and background of William Waller, I am much indebted to Roger Bird, Mike Gill, Chris Irwin, Hazel Martell and C.J. Williams. Richard Bird, Mike Blackmore, Amina Chatwin, Barry Clarke, Brian Jones and John van Laun have assisted in various ways, as have the staffs of the Ashmolean Museum, the British Library, Ceredigion Archives Service, the Royal Commission on the Ancient and Historical Monuments of Wales, The National Library of Wales, the National Museums & Galleries of Wales and Swansea University Archives. I am especially grateful to Mrs Daphne Lane, whose welcome across the threshold of Waller's old home transported me into another world and, finally, my publisher's help and encouragement must not go unrecorded.

## COMPANY OF MINE ADVENTURERS; SELECT BIBLIOGRAPHY
**(Excluding manuscript material. Compiled by Robert Protheroe Jones).**

### 1693
**William Waller**
— *A short account of Sir Carbery Pryces's lead-work … the first of June, 1693*; titled on p.2: *An abstract of the proposals of Sir Carbery Pryce and his present partners, concerning … lead-mines called Bwlchireskirhir …*
— A Mapp of the great Lead Mines of Sir Carbery Prise …

### 1698
**Anon**
— *A settlement of the mine-adventure.*
— *A settlement of the mines, late of Sir Carbery Pryse whereby the old lease is renewed and a better constitution established …*
— *An answer to a paper published by one Bateman against the mine- adventure …*
— *An answer to several objections against the mine-adventure*
— *The form of the insurance proposed in the mine-adventure*
— *A true copy of several affidavits and other proofs of the largeness and richness of the mines, late of Sir Carbery Pryse …*
**Thomas Bateman**
— *An answer to the postscript of a paper, publish'd by Sir H.M. …, intitul'd An answer to several objections against the mine- adventure.*
**Sir Humphrey Mackworth**
— *A new abstract of the mine- adventure: or, an undertaking, advantageous for the publick good …*
— *The mine-adventure; or, An expedient, first for composing all differences between the partners of the mines …*
— *The mine-adventure; or an undertaking, advantageous for the publick good …*
**William Waller**
— *An essay on the value of the mines, late of Sir Carbery Price …*

### 1700
**Company of Mine Adventurers**
— *An abstract of the present sate of the mines of Bwlchyr-Eskir-Hyr …*
— *The second abstract of the state of the mines of Bwlchyr-Eskir-Hyr …*
— *The third abstract of the state of the  mines of Bwlchyr-Eskir-Hyr… .*
**William Shiers**
— *A familiar discourse or dialogue concerning the mine- adventure*

### 1701
**Company of Mine Adventurers**
— *The fourth abstract of the state of the mines of Bwlchyr-Eskir-Hyr …*

### 1702
**Company of Mine Adventurers**
— *A short account of the proceedings of the select committee of the mine-adventurers for lengthening their term and enlarging their boundaries …*
**William Waller**
— *An essay on the value of mines, late of Sir Carbery Price …* a reprint of the 1698 work

### 1704
**William Waller**
— *A Description of the Mines in Cardiganshire*
— *Honour'd sirs, it is not for the vanity of appearing in print,* … same contents as *A Description of the Mines in  Cardiganshire*

### 1705
**Company of Mine Adventurers**
— *An account of the clear profits of extracting silver out of lead ...*
**Sir Humphrey Mackworth**
— *Affidavits, certificates, and presentments … with respect to the irregular proceedings of several justices of the peace for the county of Glamorgan, … ;* a detached part of a pamphlet, given its own title page; not part of either of the two pamphlets below.
— *The case of Sir Humphrey Mackworth*; a different text to the pamphlet below.
— *The case of Sir Humphrey Mackworth … with respect to the irregular proceedings of several justices of the peace for the county of Glamorgan, …*
**William Shiers**
— *A familiar discourse or dialogue concerning the mine-adventure.* A different text to the work of 1700

### 1707
**Thomas Heton**
— *Some account of the mines …*
**Sir Humphrey Mackworth**
— *The case of Sir Humphrey Mackworth … with respect to the extraordinary proceedings … of … Sir Thomas Mansell …*

### 1708
**Company of Mine Adventurers**
— *An account of the proceedings of the … company … with relation to … Mr.Daniel Peck …*
— *Report of the committee appointed … the sixth day of May, 1708*

— *That the Mine Adventurers have the honour to be incorporated …* [a petition to be allowed to issue notes of credit]

**1709**
**Company of Mine Adventurers**
— *An account of the proceedings … with relation to their accounts …*
**William Shiers**
— *A familiar discourse or dialogue concerning the mine-adventure.* A different text to earlier works of this title

**1710**
**Anon**
— *A short answer to several objections against Sir Humphrey Mackworth …*
— *Mineralia adjuvanda …*
— *The case of several creditors and proprietors …*
**Company of Mine Adventurers**
— *An abstract of the deed … giving powers to fifteen persons …*
**Great Britain: Parliament**
— *Report of the committee of the House of Commons … to consider … the mine-adventure …*
**Thomas Hawkins**
— *The reply of Mr.Hawkins …*
**Sir Humphrey Mackworth**
— *A short state of the case and proceedings of the … mine-adventurers … justified by vouchers …*
— *The answer of Sir Humphrey Mackworth to several particulars …*
— *The book of vouchers …*
**William Waller**
— *The answer of Mr.Waller to Mr.Hawkins's report …*
— *The mine-adventure laid open …*

**1711**
**Anon**
— *Remarks on a paper, intitled, Observations on the bill …*
— *Reasons for the passing of the mine-adventurers bill …*
— *Reasons against passing the bill relating to the mine-adventurers …*
— *The case of the united society, for the improvement of mineral works …*
**Company of Mine Adventurers**
— *Observations on the bill relating to the mine-adventurers*
— *The case of the Company of Mine-Adventurers, relating to Mrs.Lucas …*
— *The case of the creditors and proprietors … observations on the Bill …*
— *The case of the mine-adventurers. The scope of … the Bill …*
**Great Britain: Parliament**
— *An Act for the relief of the creditors … of the mine-adventurers …*

**Sir Humphrey Mackworth**
— *The second part of the book of vouchers …*

**1712**
**Anon**
— *The projector of the mine-adventure detected and laid open …*
— *The shortest way with a deputy-governor: or, observations on Mr. Forty …*
**Company of Mine Adventurers**
— *The mine-adventurers … proposal for raising a stock of 20000 l …*

**1714**
**William Waller**
— *The case of Mr. William Waller in relation to … Edward Vaughan …*

**1720**
**Anon**
— *A proposal … for raising a stock of twenty thousand pounds …*
**Company of Mine Adventurers**
— *A clear view of the fundamental constitutions … of the mine adventurers …*
— *A representation made by a committee of seventeen persons … containing a vindication of Sir Humphrey Mackworth …*
**Roderick Mackenzie**
— *A familiar letter to a gentleman at Bath …*
— *A letter to Sir J— C——, Baronet …*
**Thomas Williams & John Hopkins**
— *A view of the advantages arising … at Neath, by … making … copper, brass, lead, and iron …*

**1721**
**Company of Mine Adventurers**
— *A scheme for advancing the trading stock of the … mine-adventurers …*
— *A short account of the profit and security which all persons will enjoy who shall advance money…*
— *The advantage of the new scheme of the mine-adventurers …*
**Thomas Heton**
— *Some account of the mines …* Reprint of 1707 work
**Roderick Mackenzie**
— *Now or Never …*
**Thomas Williams & John Hopkins**
— *A view of the advantages arising … at Neath, by … making … copper, brass, lead, and iron …* Reprint of 1720 work

**OTHER MINING TITLES BY THE SAME AUTHOR**

*The Old Metal Mines of Mid-Wales*, Parts 1 – 6, 1974-1991
*Dylife – A Famous Welsh Leadmine*, 1975, 1984
*The Old Copper Mines of Snowdonia*, 1982, enlarged edition, 2003
*Frongoch Lead & Zinc Mine*, 1986, enlarged edition,1996
*The Mines of Newent and Ross*, 1987
*A History of Sygun Copper Mine*, 1987
*Lewis Morris and the Cardiganshire Mines*, 1994 (With Philip Wyn Davies)